Open to Doubt

Open to Doubt

Volume 1

Marcus Achison

Matador
9 Priory Business Park,
Wistow Road, Kibworth Beauchamp,
Leicestershire. LE8 0RX
Tel: 0116 279 2299
Email: books@troubador.co.uk
Web: www.troubador.co.uk/matador
Twitter: @matadorbooks

ISBN 978 1785899 881

British Library Cataloguing in Publication Data.
A catalogue record for this book is available from the British Library.

Printed and bound in the UK by TJ International, Padstow, Cornwall
Typeset in 11pt Aldine401 BT by Troubador Publishing Ltd, Leicester, UK

Matador is an imprint of Troubador Publishing Ltd

To Anne Wood.

Introduction

It's the book you can't put down. I've tried to put it down but I couldn't. That's why I'm still holding it. There's a lot of interesting and very odd stuff in it, and I should know because I can't put it down. There are very strange items about foreign travel, buttock maintenance, baboons, parasitic mind wasps and borstals. Other even more strange items inform us about goblins, unusual medical procedures, Yekky Doris and the truly repugnant Spawn Hog. You will find it hard to believe your very eyes when you read the pages of this truly startling book. You will read and reread the pages to try to comprehend the magnitude of the information contained therein.

Vera Mutance (Miss), Out and About Reporter for The Gubbenstery Examiner.

Mucky Nesbitt's Giraffe and Wasp Hire

In these austere days of doom and gloom, a good night out is a great distraction from the problems of everyday life. However, most parties consist of the same tired old acts. If it's not strippers, it's magicians or the despicable karaoke. Other acts such as cretin circuses, monkey wrestling, and nose jousting have been tried but proved to be too expensive. Now though, help is at hand with *Mucky Nesbitt's Giraffe and Wasp Hire*. Mucky himself has developed special breeds of giraffes and wasps that are completely at home in human company and are nearly almost safe to handle within reason. Indeed, sometimes Mucky will ride home from his laboratory astride his favourite giraffe, Bimly Smith, while wearing a full beard of wasps, many of whom he knows by name. Mucky says this is a very relaxing and eco-friendly mode of transportation despite the abuse he receives from members of the public and the numerous arrests he has had for inappropriate possession of wild beasts in a town centre. Now these giraffes and wasps are available for hire at reasonable prices for birthday parties, leaving dos, bar mitzvahs and all manner of celebrations.

Prices start at £100.02 per giraffe per week and £100.01 per box of 500 raging wasps per day.
Wasps are supplied in a cardboard box (with breathing holes).
Giraffes are supplied in a larger cardboard box (with larger breathing holes).

Creature food is included in the price for an additional one-off payment of £39.
Candy floss and ice cream are supplied for the giraffes.
Flowers, anchovies and cheese puffs are supplied for the wasps.

"A real bargain, I thoroughly endorse Mucky's products," Ruth Squalid.

"Never again, I was stung from head to foot and had to use a flame thrower to quell the brutal onslaught of the angry wasps," Ron Dubious.

"It was a nightmare. About fifty wasps went down my wife's throat and the giraffe kicked my dog's head off," Rear Admiral Norbert (Nobby) Quazy.

"It's a very odd concept but it worked for me, apart from the trampling and multiple stings," Sir Quiggly Gramlington (Deceased).

"Don't do it. I hired three giraffes and a thousand wasps for my son's birthday. The wasps stung everyone in the house and then set up a nest in my frail great aunt's mouth. All three giraffes stampeded and ended up in the attic after trampling my next-door neighbour to death. They had to be slaughtered by a passer-by," Captain Doreen Stupefy (Mr).

"I didn't know wasps ate cheese puffs," Oscar de la McMillan.

"I much prefer bees and wildebeest," Rory Tyrosine.

M. Nesbitt, Supplier of Items Various Ltd, 84 Bewilder Road, Spunley-on-Sea.

Holiday Choice
Recommends
The Islands of Northern Dakota

By our none-too-bright reporter *Barry Android*

This week, Holiday Choice recommends the beautiful Islands of Northern Dakota. This seldom visited vacation location is brimming with treats and things to do for the whole family. A speedy ten hour flight from Heathrow gets you to this delightful holiday destination. You will arrive refreshed at Gangpox International Airport on the dazzling island of Spewmarillow, the largest of the three magical islands of Northern Dakota. The other two islands, Spewmaglando and Spewmadando are nearby. Each island offers a wide range of activities and adventures and our intrepid reporter Barry Android went to find out more.

Spewmarillow

I arrived in Spewmarillow after a delayed 29-hour flight from Heathrow via Tokyo and Madagascar absolutely wrecked and dishevelled. The first thing I noticed on arrival was the intense heat and clouds of biting flies, and that was *inside* the terminal building. It appears that the airport was also being used as a veterinary clinic and builder's merchant, which made it very messy and filled with a strange array of yells, squawks and screeches. When I set foot outside the airport the heat became even more intolerable. I checked the temperature gauge on my watch and it read a staggering 79°C, at midnight. I was being boiled alive so I had to immediately strip naked and throw my clothes away. I hailed a taxi and ordered the driver to take me to Wild Baby Cabins Resort, my home for the next two days. I noticed the cab driver was also naked and he told me the weather had cooled down quite a bit from the previous week. I found it hard to believe that it could get any hotter. The driver drove incredibly fast through the night for about sixteen hours before dropping me at my shanty town-style log cabin. It was now four in the afternoon and the intense, bludgeoning heat seemed to affect my eyesight and I couldn't see properly, so I went straight to bed. When I awoke I was in a hospital bed surrounded by doctors and nurses and was hooked up to all sorts of bleeping machines. My eyesight seemed to be okay now and I noticed that all the doctors and nurses were naked. The consultant in charge, a Professor Dave Sperm, told me I had been brought in to A & E by the superintendent of Wild Baby Cabins, who found me lying on a dirt track bleeding from the eyes. Apparently I was very lucky to be alive and was suffering from heat exhaustion and burst eyes. I was discharged by Professor Sperm and ordered to keep my temperature down. I left the hospital, still naked, and boarded the overnight ferry to Spewmaglando.

Spewmaglando

The voyage across the Sea of Prandy to Spewmaglando took over thirty hours and was a terrifying crossing. The wind was high and the sea was raging with colossal 90-foot waves crashing over the deck. We ran aground on sandbanks twice, collided with two other ships, one of which sank, and finally crashed into the pier at over thirty knots on our arrival at Spewmaglando Island. Several passengers were injured, the bow of the ship came off and two giant poodles drowned. I climbed onto the pier, miraculously with only a broken nose and two black eyes, where I had been kicked by a terrified escaped mule that ran amok on deck. The minute I arrived on Spewmaglando, the rain stopped, the wind dropped and the sun came out. The heat picked up rapidly and once more I found myself being baked alive. I was already naked, so I couldn't cool down by taking my clothes off. I decided to seek the shade of a large mango tree to give myself time to gather my senses. The minute I sat down, I was bitten on the upper lip by a mountain lion and copiously sprayed by a massive skunk. For supposedly being on holiday, I was in a right state. My black eyes had swollen to nearly shut, my broken nose was blocked and I could hardly breath, my upper lip was streaming blood by the gallon and I was absolutely stinking of skunk piss. I decided to make my way to the caravan that was booked for me at the oddly named Killer Bee Recreational Vehicle Park. I was so hot and uncomfortable by this time that I decided to rent a large refrigerated truck to take me to the caravan park. The journey should have taken no more than thirty minutes but two days later I was still in the back of the truck. I was just about frozen to death and about to inhale my last breath when the back door opened and the driver announced casually that I was at my destination. I wanted to ask him what had taken so long but my tongue had swollen to the size of a basketball and I couldn't speak. He eventually dragged me out of the truck, carried me to my caravan and put me to bed. I couldn't move so I just lay there and fell asleep. When I finally woke up I found myself once more in the intensive care ward of a hospital with about twenty naked doctors and nurses standing around me. Before I could say a word, one of the doctors told me I had fallen asleep, started sleepwalking and ended up staggering into a nest of killer bees. I could now add frostbite, cracked ribs, a dislocated kneecap and over four hundred killer bee stings to my growing list of ailments. I was in agony and stank to high heaven but they said they needed the beds so I was released. The very second I exited the hospital I was once more pummelled by the sun. The air was so hot and thick I thought I was going to vomit up my ribcage. My watch read 81°C, as the sweat on my brow became a torrent.

I hailed a cab and the naked driver drove to the airport where I boarded the 7pm flight to Spewmadando.

Spewmadando

My flight was late, due to a burst tyre and missing wing, but once that was sorted we took off and began our thirty minute island hop over the Sea of Cowbag to Spewmadando Island and the continuation of my vacation. We immediately encountered extreme turbulence and quite a few passengers, who were not wearing their seatbelt, were bounced off the ceiling of the plane and killed outright. We then flew into a tropical storm and flipped upside down, before the pilot regained control. Just as the flight was settling down, we crashed into a huge flock of geese, which destroyed the engines and we started plummeting to the ground. The pilot reassured us and said the aircraft was designed to be hit by geese and plummet towards the ground. He managed to glide the plane onto the runway, albeit at eight hundred miles per hour. The landing was heavy and I lost all my upper teeth and bit through my tongue, but I survived. I went for a walk in downtown Spewmadando in an attempt to see the sights but this was proving to be the hottest island of the three. I could hardly stand. My legs had turned to jelly and I had run out of sweat and my head was pounding. I went into a bar and ordered a glass of milk and a 5-pound slice of blue cheese. I then moved on to whisky, vodka and beer and ended up totally legless in only fifteen hours. The last thing I remember is setting fire to the bar and passing out. A month later I woke up at my desk in the offices of Holiday Choice and wrote up my report on the Islands of Northern Dakota. It truly is an exciting place to visit and is very relaxing with guaranteed year-round beautiful weather. It has an excellent transportation system and you can travel across all three islands cheaply and efficiently. The people are friendly and the wildlife is enchanting. My advice would be to get yourself over there before it becomes too commercialised and loses its charm.

Advanced Dentistry Tuition

Gubbenstery's wealthiest couple, Lucinda and Humphrey Gabardine-Smyth are proud to announce the arrival of their first child. Mortimer Gabardine-Smyth (the third) was born eighteen years ago but the butler forgot to put the ad in the paper.

Coal-fired Rocking Horse with real horse inside for sale. Thirty feet high and sixty feet long. Would suit any outsized child. Comes with year's supply of coal and hay. Phone Miss Josephine Le Margarine right away on Gubbenstery 1234.

Huge variety of spare parts available at incredible prices. Why not come and make a day of it? Free parking, free food and a free pregnant tabby cat when you spend more than £5. We are situated adjacent to the waste ground across from the zonce.

Gymnast for hire. Will climb all over your house, inside and out. Can leap from cooker to fridge complete with mid-air summersault, swing from light fittings and balance one-legged on top of any moving dog or cat. Phone Yevgeny D'Ismount for prices.

Gubbenstery High School Choir has teamed up with local media guru Seymour Rancorous to release their second album of hymns sung in the style of the Bolivian Howler Monkey. This follows last year's collection of wedding anthems sung in the style of the stampeding African elephant.

Lonely male accountant seeks lonely female tax loss adjuster for high seas adventure in homemade wooden canoe. Must be fluent in Hebrew and whatever they speak in Madagascar. Write to Mr Neville Bland, Banal Cottage, North Tedious Avenue, East Buntyside.

News for Clowns

The most informative newsletter for the working idiot today

Edited by our in-house prankster *Cosmo Stodge*

Clown Mauled by Lion

One of the world's best-known Russian clowns was mauled yesterday by a male lion at the Moscow Circus of Clowning and Tomfoolery. Buffo the clown, real name Hamish Booginskaya, was nipping the great cat's tail with a pair of pliers for a laugh when the beast suddenly turned on him. Buffo had both kneecaps bitten off but suffered no other injuries. Simba the lion, real name George Henderson, claimed that he had warned Buffo twice about nipping his tail. When Buffo ignored the supreme African predator for a third time he decided to teach him a lesson he wouldn't forget. Buffo has refused to press charges and hopes to keep his job after a year in traction. George the lion was reluctant to comment although he did have this to say, *"Laugh now ya fucking clown"*.

National Convention of Clowns Ends in Brawl

Police were called in last night after the Annual Glasgow Clown Convention ended in a small-scale riot. Scottish police had to send in their specialist Buffoon Squad to quell the fighting after a few of the clowns had a disagreement about big shoes. Following an evening's drinking, some of the clowns decided to see who had the biggest shoes and a scuffle broke out. Bobo the clown, real name Enrique Blapp, from Madrid threw a custard pie at Lardo the clown, real name Edgar Hapless from Stornoway, who retaliated by squirting him with his water flower. Local Glaswegian clown Jimmy Pish, real name Jimmy Pish, then waded in with a crowbar and a meat-softening hammer and raised the brawl to a whole new level. Heads were split open, eyes gouged out and testicles smashed. Nine clowns were arrested and twenty were taken to hospital. An arrest warrant has been issued for Jimmy Pish who is thought to be on the run in Kenya with his African half-brother Mr Pickles.

Top Clown Retires

One of the world's leading clowns has announced his retirement. Drampo the clown, real name Lorraine Nauseous, was the first clown to be a man with a woman's name. His retirement party was held in Tommy Tubbo's big circus tent in the village of Gloup on the beautiful island of Shetland and was attended by the world's most annoying clowns. An unexpected attendee was Ploppo the clown, real name Iris Crabtree, from Northern Bolton. Drampo and Ploppo had fallen out and had not spoken for over thirty years. Their disagreement started at Drampo's wedding where he was marrying the lady clown Cretto, real name Eliza-Jane Labia. As the happy couple drove off into the sunset Ploppo had secretly rigged their car doors to fall off, hoping to get a big laugh. Unfortunately, the doors fell off at 60mph and Cretto fell out of the car and in a freak accident was trampled to death by a runaway carthorse. However, at his big bash, Drampo decided to forgive Ploppo and the two chatted for hours while letting off stink bombs and throwing rotten eggs at other passing clowns. The evening culminated in a firework display where one of the lesser clowns, Spiffo, real name Charlie Globate, was fired from a cannon. Unfortunately, the canon was overloaded with dynamite and Spiffo was fired more than fifty miles out over the North Sea where he crashed into an oilrig and was killed. Drampo was first to announce that it was a sad loss to clowning, as he slapped a fellow clown in the face with a raw salmon.

Guttural Phlegm Game to Split

Writes our bebop freelancer *Eamon Dacknoid*

One of Britain's most successful bands, Guttural Phlegm Game, has decided to call it a day. GPG, as they are known by their millions of devoted fans, held a press conference this morning in Central London to announce their split. Hundreds of millions of fans had queued all night for a ticket to the split announcement, but only a lucky few million managed to squeeze into the Darcy Balanism Memorial Hall in Muswell Hill. Sitting at a long table made of solid gold were singer Peter Glarriet, guitarist Pustulence Brown, bassist Gavin Blimhagg, drummer Gonville Vadose and, unusually for a modern rock band, triangle player Gordon Upducky.

The band looked tired and worn out, especially Glarriet, who was drinking straight Advocaat out of a soup ladle. The other four also looked as if they had been out on one of their infamous all-night benders. Brown, dressed in a yellow leotard, was nursing a black eye and drinking mead out of a top hat. Blimhagg had arrived in only a pair of swimming trunks and had a dartboard tattooed on his chest. It appeared as if the dartboard had been well used as he was covered in blood and thousands of tiny pin pricks. Vadose was consuming whisky by the pint glass and was gnawing his way through an entire spit of kebab meat and was covered in grease from head to foot. Gordon Upducky was dressed in a smart trousers and jumper combo and looked refreshed as he sipped a china cup of herbal mint tea. The adventures and misadventures of GPG are the stuff of legend and have been widely publicised over their thirty-year career.

As a young band starting out in 1983, their heady mix of catchy tunes, good looks and heavy drinking soon got them noticed. Their first ever gig at the Gubbenstery Civic Centre on the 4th of August 1983 was a memorable and explosive affair. They only played ten songs, including their first single *"Exudate of the Vermin"*, but it wasn't the music that made their first gig memorable. As the band finished their last tune, the barnstorming finale, *"Scabies of the Parasitic Mites"*, one of their adoring fans climbed on stage and hugged and kissed Glarriet. The lead singer took exception to this intrusion and attacked the blond teenager with a scythe. Before security could intervene, Glarriet had butchered the young girl into over a hundred pieces as he was egged on by the baying crowd. After a ticking off from the local constabulary, Glarriet treated the crowd to an impromptu encore and premiered two of their new songs, *"Bacterium of the Mind"* and *"My Virulent Convulsion"*, both of which were future number ones. Glarriet also agreed to play a gig in the dead girl's parents' house, with all the proceeds going to charity. However, at the end of the gig, the band set fire to the house and burnt it to the ground.

No GPG tour was complete without an episode of madness from notorious hell-raising guitarist Pustulence Brown. While touring Argentina and Bolivia in 1986, the band had two days off and found themselves at a loose end. As the rest of the band headed to the beach at Comodoro Rivadavia to try out their new harpoon guns, Brown went to the local market and bought the world's most powerful guitar amplifier, the 1000-watt Augmenter F1. It took six men to get the amp back to Brown's top floor hotel suite and he immediately plugged it in and let rip. As he played the first two chords of *"Brucellosis Blues"*, the sheer power of the amp blew the top off the hotel and fired Brown fifty yards onto the main road where he was hit by a local bus. Brown was taken to hospital with cuts and bruises but ended up being forcibly ejected by hospital security after breaking into the pharmacy. Back at the hotel, no one had been killed but about fifty people had sustained head injuries from falling masonry. However, a herd of about 100 llamas in an adjacent field were killed by a combination of flying roof slates and fright.

In 1990, while touring Cameroon, the band were due to play their final gig in the capital Yaoundé when an infamous incident took place. The boys had run out of hard drugs and bassist Gavin Blimhagg and drummer Gonville Vadose were notorious for needing vast quantities of drugs to sustain their dynamic style of live playing. Glarriet and Brown were already zonked from an afternoon game of drink the bar dry and triangle player Gordon Upducky was pressing dried flowers in his room. Blimhagg and Vadose left the hotel to score some drugs and apparently imbibed far too much of some highly potent, mind-altering African narcotic that they had never encountered before. As the story goes, Glarriet, Brown, Upducky and the rest of the well-to-do guests at the five star Golden Ringworm Hotel were more than taken aback at the sight of Blimhagg and Vadose sitting astride two longhorn cows at the front of a herd of about 100 cattle, which they proceeded to stampede through the luxury hotel. They careered through the hotel from the bottom all the way up to the twentieth floor, where the boys had their luxury penthouse. When they reached the penthouse they just kept on going and charged their way through the safety railings on the balcony and led the whole terrified herd over the edge to plummet the 390-feet into the swimming pool below. The swimming pool and patio area was a scene of carnage with drowned cows, petrified guests and fragments of bovine carcass covering the entire area. Amazingly, Blimhagg and Vadose had ridden their cows all the way down and were still sitting astride them when they clambered out of the shallow end of the pool. Police quickly arrived at the scene but let the boys off with a caution. The whole band then went on to play one of their best ever gigs at the Yaoundé Lyceum.

As the journalists and TV reporters began to question the band about their reasons for splitting up, each member of the group gave different reasons. Glarriet wanted to enter rehab, Brown wanted to enter rehab to get well enough to take even more drugs, Blimhagg wanted to open a quiet country shop specialising in guns and dynamite, Vadose was keen to join the armed conflict in Luxembourg to fight on the side of the Neo-Protestant Catholic guerrilla faction and Upducky said he was keen to publicise triangle playing in Kenya and Greenland. As the questioning of the band continued and the level of wailing and sobbing by distraught fans increased, the members of GPG grew increasingly fidgety and uncomfortable as they sat at their enormous gold table. They had consumed all the alcohol they had brought to the press conference and had sent a runner to acquire emergency supplies from the local supermarket. All of a sudden, the entire band and their manager, Arthur Spanzian, went into a huddle and started muttering to one another out of earshot of the reporters. This continued for an hour before Spanzian said that front man Peter Glarriet had an announcement to make. Glarriet slowly rose to his feet and said that after a deep and meaningful discussion with all the band members, Guttural Phlegm Game had decided to reform. The cheering and whooping of the crowd nearly took the roof off the old Memorial Hall as fans celebrated. Glarriet asked the crowd for hush as he announced that their comeback gig would start in five minutes. All the boys suddenly jumped up on top of the gold table and stripped naked. Roadies came running in with their instruments and the lights dimmed. The five stark naked rock icons then launched into an ear-splitting live rendition of their comeback single *"Ablation of the Mind Cyst"*.

Gubbenstery College

New Courses now available

Gubbenstery College is proud to announce the launch of several new courses. Following a kind donation of one hundred million pounds by the well-known multimillionaire inventor Sir Bertrand Pallid, we now offer an unrivalled miscellany of new and fascinating courses leading to almost degree-like qualifications. Sir Bertrand, who invented the unfledged pigeon (squab) display cabinet, self-cleaning tights and his world-leading range of flavoured curtains, has insisted that his donation be spent wisely on new courses found in no other university, and not frittered away on long term development of the college. Two of our most exciting new courses are listed below.

Urban Dog Training Techniques (Theory and Practice)

You will be taught how to round up dogs on the streets of quiet neighbourhoods using all available modern techniques. Dogs, particularly ones minding their own business, will be chased, cornered and goaded into making a mistake, where upon they will be seized and put into a metal dustbin ready for repatriation to a designated safe zone. Experienced lecturers will instruct you on how to safely release the dogs into a confined area where they will undergo familiarization training. Familiarizing experts will teach you how to burst paper bags loudly, bang cymbals together, let off loud fireworks and then reward the dogs with bowls of lard and lettuce. Applicants must be good at running and be able to laugh out loud.
(Contact: Professor Nedrick Cuspidor on Gubbenstery 7070).

Combined Witchcraft, Jujuism and Necromancy

Learn all the wonders of Witchcraft, both real and imagined, and prepare yourself for a dazzling future career in the exciting world of terrible goings-on. You will learn the basics such as spells, hexes and newt dissection, before moving on to more advanced techniques such as growing your own warts, cauldron preparation, shrinking people and cackling. As you progress through the various stages of the course, your former friends and associates will find your presence more and more alarming and disconcerting, and this will be a tribute to your dedication to the dark arts. Finally, you will be instructed by experts how to perform much more hair-raising and startling wizardry, such as raising the dead, hocus-pocus, gobbledygook and mumbo jumbo.

(Contact: Dame Clarinda de Spittoon at dcds@bmagic.voodoo).

Other new and exhilarating courses coming soon:

- Advanced High Jinx and Escapades
- Introduction to Coshing, Bludgeoning and Clubbing
- The History of Gutlessness and Spinelessness
- Lilliputian Business Administration for Dwarves and Pygmies
- The Poems and Essays of Vic Drubbing
- Intermediate Deception, Hoaxing and Swindling
- Sawdust Appreciation (Level 3)

This advert is sponsored by Radio Gubbenstery, 101.5 FM *"We Mo Be There."*

Reasonable Breakfast Opportunities

Book Sale at Janice Skonko's Book Outlet. New titles include: Cookery for Maniacs, Anti-Boring Tips for New Mums, Poetry for Reptiles, Learning for Idiots (Volumes 1 – 6,000) and The Bumper Book of Lying Politicians. We are open every August at 4am. Find us at 19 Lovepod Ave, Gubbenstery.

Big fat man called Big Herbert Lardex seeks friendship of big woman called Big Joyce and big horse called Big Harold for extensive girlie and equine adventures on a daily basis. Email:herbert@nutjob.co.uk.

Local priest and part-time bow and arrow salesman Father Lucifer O'Devil would like his congregation to be made aware that from next Friday he will be known as Father Lucifer O'Princeofdarkness, or simply "Lou" to all his favourite parishioners.

East Buntyside resident "Mad" Johnny Ballcake would like to know if any of you sissies from Gubbenstery fancied a fight on Saturday night. If so, meet me behind the gasworks at midnight ya bunch of fairies.

Massive collection of illegitimate children for sale. Ages range from 1 – 60 and all are certified legal in Belgium and Chad. Simply turn up, fill out the form and pick one. Everyone loves a child for Christmas, but hurry, they're selling fast! Visit Kiddyworld at Unit 6, Bastard Business Park, Southwest East Buntyside.

Economically priced collection of children's toys, such as dolls, racing cars, footballs, catapults, jackhammers and buzz saws all exquisitely crafted from delicious English corned beef. Call in to our fully refrigerated Toy Emporium at 92 Ringworm Street, Gubbenstery.

Ask Marjorie!
Let Agony Aunt Marjorie Fetid solve your problems

Dear Marjorie,

I am a 59 year-old woman and I am unable to play the piano. What do you suggest?
Nora Spunty, Renfrew.

Marjorie says:

Well Nora, looks like you've got quite a problem. I could play the piano by the time I was twelve, so you're in a tight spot. I suggest you learn to play the piano.

Dear Marjorie,

I am a 59 year-old woman and can't find my dildo anywhere. I told my mum but she refuses to buy me a new one, so I'll need to buy one myself. What type do you suggest?
Phyllis Bunnery, Cheadle Hulme.

Marjorie says:

The one I use is the Power Plunger and it does the trick, although I think there is a new one on the market which is more powerful called the Mighty Impaler. Let me know how you get on.

Dear Marjorie,

I am a 59 year-old man and would like to hire some wasps and possibly a giraffe for my daughter's ruby wedding anniversary. Any ideas? **Digby Dratiss, Garstank.**

Marjorie says:

That's an easy one Digby. Write to my friend Mucky Nesbitt at 84 Bewilder Road, Spunley-on-Sea. Mention my name and he'll sort you out.

Dear Marjorie,

I am a 59 year-old man who loves ginger biscuits but my 59-year old slob of a wife keeps eating them all. What should I do? **Dorian Vajina, Bratislava.**

Marjorie says:

That's a tough one Dorian. You will either have to buy a bigger tin of biscuits or get a divorce. Alternatively, you could acquire a handgun and shoot your wife just above the ear.

Dear Marjorie,

I am an 18 year-old girl and I think my boyfriend is cheating on me with my mum and dad. When I come home from work, he's in bed with either my mum or my dad. He says there's nothing going on and they are just chatting, but it doesn't seem right to me. My mum is 89 and my dad is 90 and my boyfriend is 73. What should I do? **Tanya Bulbous, Old Kilpatrick.**

Marjorie says:

There's no need to worry Tanya. This is a common occurrence and should be treated in a light-hearted and jovial manner. Your boyfriend probably is chatting to your mum and dad and perhaps they get a bit chilly and decide to continue their conversation in bed. I think you should get into bed with them and make a night of it.

Write to Marjorie at 1,999,000b Bloodbath Boulevard, Upper East Buntyside.

Community News
New Centre Opens

By our disagreeable reporter *Alfonso Bubbity*

Crowds estimated to be in the numbers packed the streets of Cornwall yesterday to celebrate the grand opening of the brand new Bernard E. Lutt Centre for Japes, Tricks and Practical Jokes. The Centre was paid for by a donation of £39,000,000 by the amateur magician and cat owner Bertie Fog, although the Centre is not named after him. The 90,000-seat centre is named after the renowned businessman and partial carpet fitter Bernard E. Lutt. Local Council leaders decided that Mr Fog didn't have a good enough name to attach to the magnificent new building and therefore decided that Mr Lutt, a renowned carpet fitter and partial businessman would get the honour.

The new Centre will focus on cheering up the local community and aims to put a smile on the face of all who enrol in the vast number of courses and events. Expert funsters, tricky people and practical joke maestros have been flown in from all over the world to lend their expertise to the project.

Squeaky La Bam, the famous Argentinean jokester, will be running a course on classics, including stink bomb manufacture, sneezing powder delivery and exploding cigarettes. The 59 year-old will also be running field courses in mirth making, where innocent members of the general public will be set upon out of the blue and doused in boiling treacle. Heading up the Department of Elaborate Practical Jokes or DOEPJ, will be none other than convicted arsonist Sir Gilbert Flames, who will be focusing mainly on the burning of large buildings, while people are still in them. The Conjuring and Sleight of Hand Department, or CASOHD, will be overseen by Dr Keith Baptism. Dr Baptism, who specialises in conning elderly people out of their savings and pickpocketing in the high street, will also teach mail order fraud and entry level dove handling.

A delighted Mayor, The Right Honourable Timmy Minion, cut the tape and declared the Centre open. When asked what he thought of it he replied, *"Why have we built this? What use is it?"* Lead architect on the project, Sir Dan Marzipan, commented, *"What's the point of it? It's a waste of money"*. Local church leader, Father Bonzo O'Diatribe, said, *"It is a great day for Cornwall"* and that he had signed up for most of the courses. Father O'Diatribe also said that he would be encouraging his parishioners to enrol in many of the courses in an attempt to broaden their horizons and make them happier people. As he put it, *"It'll help to reduce my workload on a Sunday. They're a right miserable bunch. I have to end every sermon with the announcement,*

"Oh why don't you lot cheer up for fuck's sake." The Ultra Reverend Kenny Piglet from a rival church said he had his own plans to cheer up his congregation. Every second Sunday he will be preaching his sermon in semaphore while juggling full size swans made from butter.

Work has already started across the road from the Lutt building on a new £12,000 Academy for Juggling, Unicycling and Tightrope Walking and it should be completed in the New Year. Local resident and mum-of-six, Brenda Loathsome, commented, *"Both buildings are a load of fucking shite"*.

Aviation News

Keeping you aware of what's in the air

Sourced by our aircraft aficionado *Colin Puppy*

New regulations come in to force today at London's Heathrow airport concerning passengers who arrive late for flights. Due to the annoyance caused to staff and other passengers, latecomers will not be allowed on board. Also, people who can't be bothered to turn up on time will be put into quarantine for six months in a cage with a gorilla and a cobra. They will be required to write out *"I must not be late or else"* one million times on the side of a pig in crayon, in Latin, using their foot.

There was a near miss yesterday at Glasgow airport when a Boeing 747 hit a crow on landing. An eyewitness said *"The crow was coming in to land when the 747 flew right into it without taking any evasive action. If the 747 had missed the crow it would have been a near hit, but it didn't. It hit it, so it was a near miss,"* said pedantic local man Tarquin Pompous. A representative of the crow's family said *"squawk"*.

Liberogambian Airways have announced that as from next Saturday night they will be serving a choice of boiling, frozen or liquefied English corned beef on all its flights. No other food, snacks or drinks will be available, said commercial director Gideon Mandingo. *"We are responding to the demands of the modern traveller,"* added Mandingo a minute later. *"English corned beef is just so delicious,"* added Mandingo two minutes later.

The world's longest serving baggage handler retired yesterday. Alfred Poponce, who is 119 years old, finally hung up his baggage handling gloves after 109 years continuous service at East Buntyside Airport. Alfred handled his first bag, a brown leather dildo case, on the first of April 1905, which was the only cargo on the first ever flight to use the new airport. Flight AD001 of Air Dubious departed East Buntyside at 11:00am and landed at Northeast Buntyside at 11:01am. The only two passengers on that historic first flight were a snobby women going away for a dirty weekend and a 16 year-old asthmatic pig heading for the slaughterhouse. Alfred is planning a long and happy retirement hiking in the foothills of the Himalayas.

A Glaswegian man was yesterday forcibly removed from a flight between London and Manchester for saying *"By the way"* too many times. Mr Angus Macaroon of 99 Luftballons Road, Glasgow, was ejected from the aircraft in Cape Town after other airports refused permission for the Pandy Airlines flight to land. Glamorous flight attendant LaDerriere McKinnon said *"The guy finished every sentence with "by the way" and it was driving me mad, so we decided to offload the fucker"*. Last week Pandy Airlines ejected an Australian girl at the North Pole for turning every sentence into a question.

An experienced pilot was fired yesterday for gross incompetence. Captain Buster Loco, 59, of Clydeside Airlines is accused of firing up a barbeque in the cockpit during a flight from New York to Glasgow. It is alleged that Captain Loco had the barbeque on full and was cooking steaks, sausages and tuna just behind the co-pilot's seat. The co-pilot, Miss Hazel Monkeynuts, said she couldn't believe her eyes when Captain Loco started setting up the barbeque. *"I couldn't believe my eyes,"* said the plump 21 year-old first officer. Suspicions were aroused when passengers noticed clouds of black smoke escaping under the cockpit door. One passenger, Mr Sebastian Mutton, said he thought there was a fire in the cockpit and went to investigate. At that point Captain Loco opened the door and offered him a sirloin steak. Mr Mutton said he initially ate the steak and it was excellent but that wasn't the point. Mutton went on, *"If it wasn't for Miss Monkeynuts squatting on the red-hot barbeque and peeing on it to extinguish it, everyone could have perished"*. Loco eventually landed the plane ahead of schedule at Glasgow and was taken away by a team of doctors and police. In his defence Captain Loco said *"I always have a barbeque on a Sunday"*.

Thrust Airlines are to continue their policy of banning certain groups of people from their aircraft. Following on from their ban on babies and pregnant women, Thrust has now issued a total ban on religious leaders and their followers. Thrust's managing director, Happy McAdam, 59, issued the following statement: *"We got rid of those screaming kids and boring pregnant women with nothing to say apart from mind-numbing baby talk. We thought it was time to rid ourselves and other innocent passengers of annoying religious people with their muttering and praying at the first sign of turbulence. We want to create a beautiful, atheist, noise-free and interesting experience for our passengers."* Thrust Airlines deny that they are considering banning people who talk too much and escaped murderers.

Gubbenstery airport has been given the go-ahead for a major expansion. Airport manager Cecil Rangoon says this will allow Gubbenstery airport to develop into a twenty first century airport. There will be a new second runway and later on a third, fourth and fifth runway to accommodate any future increase in air traffic. Rangoon has rubbished suggestions that all the new runways are not needed because there is only one flight a day from Gubbenstery to East Buntyside. *We're building for the future,"* he said. The new terminal building will also feature a state-of-the-art Monkey Centre for visiting monkeys of all types to meet. There will be a supermarket, 20-screen cinema complex, ice rink, 10,000-room hotel and a brand new anal bleaching complex. The airport will be surrounded by a 1000-foot deep moat filled with one of every sea and river creature in the world. Rangoon says he wanted Gubbenstery International Airport to be different to all the bland airports around the world. It is with that in mind that he personally developed a system where all passengers will be delivered to their aircraft by log flume. He accepts that passengers will arrive in the aircraft soaking wet and probably injured but says that they won't mind because they'll be in holiday mood. Protesters claim it is a complete waste of money, although they are in favour of the anal bleaching complex.

Mandrake Airways is the first airline in the world to remove all seating from their aircraft and have standing only. They claim it will dramatically cut costs and that's what people want. Chairman Peter Horseboy said a Boeing 737 that used to carry 150 people in seats can now carry 5,000 standing up. Instead of a return fare from London to Toronto being £600, it is now £599. *"That's a saving of a pound and who wouldn't want that,"* added Horseboy. Suggestions by The Health and Safety Department that it is dangerous and unhygienic are answered by Horseboy who says, *"People should easily be able to last 8 or 9 hours without eating or going to the toilet and they can always doze standing up"*. A feasibility study on a seat-free flight from New York to Sydney showed that more than half the 5,000 passengers survived.

A body found in the foothills of the Himalayas yesterday was confirmed as retired baggage handler Alfred Poponce of East Buntyside. He was apparently punched to death and robbed by a beautiful but highly unpredictable mountain gorilla.

Exciting New Rabbit Recipes

Enjoy all the fun of a farming day out with a day down on the farm. Visit Obadiah McPot's fully working farm and have a day to remember. After getting up at 4am, you will learn to spread animal faecal matter over the main road, create traffic jams by travelling at 2mph in a filthy tractor, drink buttermilk, eat mice and rats, shoot burglars in the face and cross-dress convincingly. For full details email omcpot@oharrrr.bullsemen.uk.

Sporting equipment fully fashioned from succulent and delicious English corned beef. We have dart boards, chess boards, surf boards, sideboards, footballs, javelins and polo mallets, all hand crafted by our time-served corned beef technicians. Spend over £60,000 and qualify for a free half ounce tin of gorgeous English corned beef worth £5 for only £10 + VAT. Visit our website at Beefosport.com for a free catalogue for only £21.99 + VAT.

Relatively thick man (32, no hair, split lip, with hole through upper arm and lolling tongue) seeks equally thick woman (between 31 and 33, non-talker, seven feet tall, no sense of humour and tattoo of filing cabinet on upper arm) for fun and days out to libraries, bus stations and slaughterhouses. Phone Chief Superintendent Larry Cracker on Gubbenstery 9876 or email me at larcrack@polis.com or write to 91 Upper Tostong Street, Gubbenstery.

Stewing lessons now available at Gubbenstery College of Boiling and Stewing. Receive expert tuition in stewing beef, pork, cats, hens, rubber, wood, bodies and automotive parts. No water needed. All our stewing is performed using molasses super-heated to 5,000°C in a big pot. Learn advanced stirring, tasting, heavy pot lifting and the words of the Dutch national anthem. For timetable, phone Professor Jeff Glorrian on Gubbenstery 9999.

"I gave it to my dog and now he climbs trees," Ted Pug.

"These Monkey Oils certainly work for me," Dicky Plarimbo.

"I apply Monkey Oil to both my buttocks at night," Noreen Splarse.

"What about the poor wee monkeys?" Quentin Gouth.

"It doesn't tell you what it's for," Jethro P. Yannery.

"I gave it to my cat and now he only eats nuts," Ted Pug.

"I used to use Sloth Cream to clean my eyes but now I use Monkey Oil," Len Oviduct.

The University of Gubbenstery

Department of Advanced Porcine Chaos Theory

List of Departmental Seminars

Professor Patsy Blorange – Spurious College of Beef Variant Technology
"The Role of English Corned Beef in the Diet of Pigs Being Trained as Guide Pigs for Partially Sighted Horses"

Partially sighted, one-eyed and cross-eyed horses seem to prefer working with pigs that have been exclusively fed on English corned beef. Professor Blorange discusses the benefits of English corned beef in the diet of pigs. Recent wayward results are presented by Patsy.

Dr Keith Spoin – University of Southwest East Buntyside
"The Medicinal Benefits and Severe Drawbacks of Drinking Boavis"

Boavis is the controversial restorative drink made by the reclusive monks of North Prumpo Abbey on the outskirts of Glord. The ingredients of Boavis are a closely guarded secret and are known only to the head monk, Brother Frannypoos McGillicuddy. Some people have claimed that Boavis has cured them of leprosy, bunions and mountain goat vomiting syndrome. Others have blamed their psychotic behaviour, such as eating rubber and putting hot soup in their ears, on the consumption of Boavis. Dr Spoin analyses the data.

Dr Trevor Goopy – The Jewish University of Pippitypoppity
"Is Mashed Pig a Viable Alternative to Mashed Potato?"

Dr Goopy discusses the outcome of a full scale clinical trial comparing mashed pig to mashed potato in families with more than 12 children. The problems of such a complex trial are discussed. Trevor explains how he overcame such problems as people's initial fear of eating mashed potato, the difficulty of mashing up a pig in a normal teacup and the incessant squealing and oinking.

Mr Jeremiah Ballruss – The College of Advanced Piffle
"Is Great Britain so Great if it is Being Overrun by Simpletons?"

Leading mind surgeon Jeremiah Ballruss discusses the increase in the number of dolts, idiots and general simpletons in Britain today. His team have harvested over 5,000 simpletons from the streets of Britain and attempted to cure them of idiocy using various methods. He initially tried using education, monetary incentives and persuasive techniques to make them slightly more sensible, but this showed little success. Eventually, Mr Ballruss discovered that severe beatings soon did the trick. Jeremiah explains this cutting edge technique.

Professor Pustula Smith – The Institute of Pig and Boar Thermodynamics
"Are Swine More Suited to the High Jump or the Long Jump?"

Professor Smith explains her unorthodox studies and attempts to justify her belief that allowing animals to compete in athletics events would make for a fairer society. Her early findings include video footage of pigs and wild boar training for the high jump and long jump by being thrown off high buildings. She also has very special news of Burpo the Cheetah's attempt at a new world record in the 100m.

Dr Morag Blim – The School of Multicultural Broth Analysis
"An In Depth Study of the Benefits of This and That"

Dr Blim uses her vast experience of broth, soup and mirepoix-based consommé analysis to explain the findings of her latest 5-year study. The Blimeister General has been looking at the effects of replacing free school milk for 5-10 year-old children with paraquat. Momo's results are earth-shattering and she was recently awarded the Cock-a-leekie medal for her services to amalgamated blended nutrients.

Dr Roger Trousers – Glord School of Home Economics for Young Ladies
"Proper Use of the Slaughtered Swine at Dinner Parties"

Dr Trousers discusses the great amount of unnecessary waste generated from the slaughter of pigs. He claims that discarding all four legs and the body of the pig is a diabolical liberty. He then explains that using only the pig's head for food is an insult to the pig. Roger will then perform his famous party trick of forcing an entire pig's anus into his mouth while knitting a woollen condom using only his feet. Doc Trousers will then be awarded his Pig Spokesperson of the Year Award by Dame Nancy Clawball.

Dame Enid Spoth – Gubbenstery Institute of Train of Thought
"A Modern Approach to Banana-Straightening Techniques"

The current approach to dealing with misshapen fruit by rejecting it is examined in great detail by Enid Spoth, while she simultaneously sings Bundeshymne, the Austrian National Anthem. Dame Spoth's remarkably fragrant breath will ensure that everyone in the audience will have a jolly time.

Professor Louis Skidmarque – Institute de Sans Pantalon de Paris
"The Effects of Strong Lager (9% ABV) on the Mindoro Warty Pig"

The effects of alcohol on Swine was studied over a 30-year period by Professor Skidmarque and his team of scientists and hernia truss salesmen. His preliminary findings show that under the influence of strong lager, the Mindoro Warty Pig will climb scaffolding, eat concrete, wear a hat and jump out of open bedroom windows. Professor Skidmarque believes that this proves that there is a common ancestor linking pigs that regularly consume strong lager with the modern city-dwelling human idiot.

Dr Becky Lionbarr – The University of Structural and Mechanical Bloating
"The Advantages of being a Hippopotamus"

The much derided comedy animal the hippopotamus has been closely studied by Dr Lionbarr and her group over the past week and a half. Here she explains that not all hippopotami are created equal. Some of them are intelligent, peaceful, trustworthy animals that care for their young and mind their own business. Other hippopotami, however, are right stupid bastards. This latter group have been observed trying to head butt ants, climbing trees and attempting to swallow horses whole. Becky presents hippopotamus society as never seen before by drawing it in crayon on a very long roll of lavatory paper.

The Mystery of

The Spawn Hog

By our horrifying swine expert *Virginia Daisymouth*

On New Year's Eve 1963 a great party was taking place to celebrate the New Year at Nelipot Hall, a rainbow-coloured wood and rubber-constructed stately home in rural Galloway near Scotland. Nelipot Hall had been home to the Nelipot family for over 10,000 years and was currently the domicile of Lord Wilbur Nelipot, his wife Lady Millicent Nelipot and their daughter Mavis. Wilbur Nelipot was a tall imposing figure who always dressed in full highland dress of kilt, waistcoat, tartan high heels and a medium length blond wig. His wife Millicent was a tall and creepy woman with a bald head and a beautiful smile. She always wore a skin-tight rubber cat suit apart from on special occasions when she would wear a full suit of armour, complete with drinking straw attachment.

The Spawn Hog was a creature said by locals to haunt Nelipot Hall. They say it was created one terrible night in 1407 when the then Lord Nelipot, Rupert, made a pact with the Devil. Rupert Nelipot was a weak man and lived in fear of his domineering wife Cindy. He eventually arrived at the point of hanging himself to free himself from Cindy's abusive taunts when, it is rumoured, the Devil himself appeared in front of him and offered him an alternative.

The Devil would turn Cindy into the Spawn Hog in return for a lifetime's devotion from Rupert. Rupert enquired what a Spawn Hog was and the Devil explained. The Spawn Hog has the face of a pig and the body of the converted person. It would be under the control of Rupert and all subsequent Lords of Nelipot. Sometimes it would make itself visible to others and sometimes not. Rupert would be able to control the Spawn Hog purely by thought, as long as he remained devoted to the Devil and spurned any other worshipful master. Rupert agreed and instantly the Spawn Hog appeared before his very eyes and what a ghastly, stinking creature it was. It was six feet tall with Cindy's majestic naked body topped off with a huge, sweaty, drooling, snorting pig's head. It was a truly terrifying sight and Rupert was initially shocked before breaking into a slight giggle and then hysterically laughing at the plight of his monstrosity of a wife. At least this was the rumour among the local town's folk.

Wilbur Nelipot had always denied any knowledge of such a creature and attributed it to local gossip and folklore. His wife Millicent had heard the rumours but she too attributed them to local legend drummed up to attract visitors to the house in the summer months. The huge stately home needed paying customers to help fund the gibbon sanctuary and full size naval dockyard to the rear of the house and help to fund Wilbur and Millicent's hobby of re-enacting great historical plagues and floods.

The 1963 party was in full swing and everyone was enjoying themselves bringing in the New Year. However, for Lord Nelipot the evening soon took a turn for the worse. One of the young men from the town, who had always been pestering Mavis for a date, had turned up with some of his friends. Young Rocco Ravensblood was always a trouble maker and took great delight in attempting to woo the Lord's daughter. Wilbur had chased him away from Mavis before but the lad was persistent and this time he was drunk and making a nuisance of himself in the Great Hall. Even though he was a pest, Mavis was flattered by the attention and couldn't help herself from chatting and flirting with him. Wilbur knew he would need to keep his eye on him.

As the evening wore on, all the revellers in the Great Hall were having a great time as 1964 edged ever closer and Mavis was beginning to let her hair down a bit, as she felt the effect of the full bottle of Jack Daniels she had downed earlier. She enjoyed adventurous past-times and had rented a top of the range cement mixer and was whizzing around inside it along with a full quota of cement. She was laughing and giggling hysterically as she leapt from the cement mixer straight onto the back of her pet zebra Stripy Joe Wilson. She rode around the Great Hall at speed, trampling the odd guest but having the time of her life as her long black hair flowed majestically behind her. She suddenly jumped off Stripy Joe and landed on top of the mantelpiece. It was at this point that she decided to put some clothes on. In what seemed like a minute but was actually two minutes, Mavis returned and immediately challenged her suitor from the village to a drinking contest.

Lord Nelipot and his wife looked on in horror as their slag of a daughter caused an embarrassing scene and many of the other guests felt uneasy in the company of this 21 year-old female nutcase. Lord Nelipot strode over to where his daughter had just downed a litre of vodka in one go and was sitting on the shoulders of her newly acquired boyfriend. He demanded that she behave or she would be sent to bed. Mavis told her father to *"Go fuck a duck"* just as Rocco punched Lord Nelipot flush on the nose. Everyone in the Great Hall gasped at this outrage as a trickle of blood dripped off the end of Lord Nelipot's aristocratic beak. Wilbur of Nelipot then took a long look at his errant daughter and her contemptible paramour and said in a chilling and almost whispering tone *"Okay then Mavis, if you won't behave I'll have to deal with you and your friend using an alternative method"*. Wilbur then exited the hall via a secret panel door next to the full size statue of Robin, the Lord's childhood pet ant.

In what seemed like five minutes but was really only four, Lord Nelipot returned holding his favourite baseball bat, Old Wooden Jim. He noticed that most of the guests had left the Great Hall and were milling around the hallway, obviously disgusted at the behaviour of Mavis and Rocco, who were currently swinging naked from the magnificent Capodimonte chandelier. Concealing Old Wooden Jim behind him, the exasperated Lord requested that his daughter and associate come down from the chandelier and leave the premises. In unison the errant pair told the lord to *"Fuck right off,"* as they continued their exhilarating mayhem. Immediately Lord Wilbur swung his bat and smashed it heavily against his daughter's buttocks, knocking her off her perch. A second swing of the bat thumped brutally into Rocco's groin and he too was battered to the ground. The incensed Lord then began a ferocious series of blows to the pair, battering them from one end of the hall to the other until they suddenly decided they had pressing business elsewhere. Wilbur opened one of the splendid opalescent stained glass windows and threw the pair out. They landed with a thud and a whimper at the bottom of the 190-foot drop, one on top of the other and the disruption was over. The guests then returned to the Great Hall and restarted the festivities as Lady Nelipot came over to her husband. *"Thank heavens for that Wilbur,"* she said, *"I thought you were going to release the Spawn Hog on that noisy pair of disruptive bastards"*. *"Spawn Hog? Isn't that just folklore dreamt up by the townsfolk my dear?"* replied the smiling Lord, as he turned his gaze upwards to a tiny window where the wall meets the ceiling, to see two small piggy eyes smiling back at him.

Finance and Foreplay Tuition

Why not visit The Milk Store. We have Dry Roasted milk, Monkey milk, Pig and Piglet milk, Jellied milk and Removable milk. Coming soon, Horse milk and Collapsible milk.

Public Notice

If you have any unripe fruit or veg, you are now entitled to hand it in to any one of the 66 Government-run Ripening Shops situated around the country. This is a completely free service for the nominal fee of £16.99. For more details.

Win a family fork by answering the following question: What is the correct spelling of the word Baboon? Send your answer written clearly on a spoon to Finlay Squampo, 39 Healthboard Road, Gubbenstery.

Enjoy a great night out at *The Chewing Dog* pub. We have fine ales, custard on tap and monthly courses on personal hygiene. Take part in our nightly basketball training and 110m hurdles heats or simply chat up one of our bar staff. 55 Babyjesus Street, Eastern Glord.

For a great day out why not come and visit Les Matthews, the talking dog of Pollerang. Les will discuss any topic with you for a fiver or two tins of Houndo dog food. Phone Miss Vivian Warts on Pollerang 0101 for details and free light switch.

Selection of cutting remarks now available. Amaze your friends with your new put downs and barbed comments. Phone Geronimo McDougall a bit later on.

Important Educational Report

Ironball

Healthy Sport or Indiscriminate Slaughter?

By our violent sports reporter *Larry Masterpig*

Local authorities around the country have recently become alarmed about the growing popularity of a new sport being played in most secondary and some primary schools. The game which is causing all the concern is Ironball. This is a relatively recent addition to most school activities, although its origin is still unclear, as are most of the rules of Ironball. The main problem with Ironball is the sheer number of injuries suffered by pupils. Injuries include heavily bruised feet, cracked skulls, broken limbs, missing teeth and one case of canine distemper.

The multitude of injuries related to the playing of Ironball seems to stem from the actual rules of the game. Each school appears to play a slightly different version of Ironball but the basic premise is as follows. Two teams of five (boys, girls or mixed) endeavour to move a 10kg iron ball from one end of a 400m x 50m court to the other and then pass it through a traditional basketball hoop. Any method of moving the Ironball is allowed, so it can be thrown, carried or kicked forwards, sideways or backwards. When a player is in possession of the Ironball, players from the opposing team can try to gain possession of the Ironball by any means necessary. This can involve grabbing it, dislodging it, pushing the opponent to make him drop it or repeatedly punching and kicking the opponent to the ground until they release their bloodied grip on the Ironball.

Good players run forward carrying the Ironball in front of them. When a player from the opposing team approaches, they swing the Ironball wildly in the air like a wrecking ball, in an attempt to crash it into their opponent's head to cause as much damage as possible. The very best players can push the Ironball ahead of them quickly and bounce it off the face or head of their opponent, catch it again and keep moving forward. The current British Champions of Ironball are The Barbarous School for Delinquent Boys in Glasgow. They have played over 500 games and have never been beaten. In a recent match, they won 25-0 and all of the opposing team were stretchered off in the first 15 minutes. One boy was unconscious for a week, another broke all his ribs and the captain, Janice Ornament, bit through her own tongue and lost a nostril. It is this level of violence and mayhem that objectors to Ironball are citing as the main reason to have it banned from schools.

Defenders of the sport, such as the Headmaster of St. Pricks Holy Borstal School, Arthur Bastard, claims it builds character, installs leadership skills and provides much needed practice for the school's first aid department. Opposing Mr Bastard's view is Lady Prunella Labium, Headmistress of Our Lady of the Brassiere School for Girls. She claims most of her girls that were once developing into beautiful young women are now cruelly distorted beasts of their former selves. Few have any teeth, most have been scalped and the head girl, Arlene Gasbomb, had both her legs bitten off in a recent friendly against St. Wildebeests Secondary School of Paisley. Education chiefs will be deciding next week whether to have Ironball banned in schools completely or to slacken the rules to allow stabbing, maiming and the throwing of boiling porridge at opponents.

Borstal News

The News Bulletin for the confined youth of today

By our incarceration reporter *Arthur Ponderosa*

Gubbenstery Central Borstal has announced that four inmates tried to escape last Saturday night following a drunken party. The illegal knees-up was held in the flower arranging department of D Wing. Ned Binbag, 21, a university student studying chemistry and serving 18 months for poisoning a tadpole, allegedly manufactured super strong hooch from shoe polish, leaves and phlegm. Binbag and three others tried to escape at midnight by jumping out of a ten-storey window onto a chair, which was placed in the exercise yard earlier. However, the first three jumpers missed the chair. One of them landed next to the chair and was killed on impact. Another landed on top of a parked car and was killed on impact. The third escapee was blown off course because he was wearing big trousers and glided over the perimeter wall onto a busy road and was knocked down and killed by an ice cream van. Only Binbag managed to land on the chair, breaking both his legs and all four legs of the chair. He also ruptured his eyeballs, fractured his tongue and severely lacerated both buttocks. He has since had his sentence increased to ten years. The Governor of the GCB, Mr Barry Yoothanazia, says steps have been taken to sweep up all leaves, terminate the use of shoe polish, collect all phlegm and ban all chemistry students from using the state-of-the-art borstal chemistry labs.

The chairman of East Buntyside Reform School for Bad Boys, Mr Declan Pamby, has announced a record intake of boys in the last semester. Usually the EBRSFBB would expect an intake of about 20 boys per semester but the most recent intake was 300. Boys aged between 10 and 40 can be incarcerated for crimes ranging from stealing sweets to international genocide. However, the bulk of the boys are in for arson, stealing chocolate bars and setting fire to chocolate bars. When asked his opinion on the large volume of new recruits Mr Pamby said, *"This is fantastic news. It demonstrates that we are really making a big effort in the production of thugs and miscreants in this country. We should be proud."*

Glord Detention Centre has been locked down for the foreseeable future due to the escape of a prisoner. Nineteen year-old Ned Gubbity was reported missing yesterday morning when he failed to show up for one of his rehabilitation training courses. Gubbity had one more session to attend at his advanced head butting and knife wielding class and was considered a model student. However, following an incident with another inmate, he failed to show up and the alarm was raised. Later, staff found evidence of an escape. Apparently Gubbity had phoned a rental car company to deliver a car outside the main gate. He then parachuted off the top of the building using bed sheets and landed outside. He made off in the rental car and has not been seen since. Unsubstantiated reports claim he was sighted in a hardware shop in Glasgow. According to the shop owner, Sheldon Gonko, 59, Gubbity bought four sets of butcher knives. Police have reminded the public what to do if they see Gubbity. Tackle him head on using maximum aggression and kick him senseless until he is subdued. Once he has been trounced and tied up, take him along to the local police station.

One of the newest youth correctional facilities opened last week in Western Skonkage. The Reformatory for Distasteful Women opened its doors last Tuesday and replaces the outdated Skonkage Home for Abhorrent Ladies. The new facility is intended to house obnoxious girls aged 8-18 and will focus on retribution rather than rehabilitation. The newly appointed governor of the facility Mrs Shirley Monoblart said that any young women brought to the institution will be battered, beaten and bludgeoned in a fair and respectful manner. *"These errant females have done bad things and it is our duty to exact revenge and punish them without pity. It's what the public would expect,"* said Mrs Monoblart yesterday with just a hint of a smile on her face.

The entire population of Blurting's Borstal for Repugnant Boys and Girls has come down with amoebic dysentery. The correctional institution, which opened in 1921 and is famous for its leniency, is now a no-go area, except for some medical staff dressed in protective clothing. Tropical disease experts from the Brian Yamamoto Institute in Helsinki think they have discovered the source of the infection. Apparently the Governor, Mr Iain Vomitito, 59, arranged a surprise birthday party for one of the inmates and as a special treat had a dead horse flown in from China to be roasted on a spit over a large bonfire. The horse, a 36 year-old stallion called Ming the horse, had mysteriously collapsed and died, so the owner put it up for sale. Mr Vomitito bought the horse for £2 after seeing an advertisement in the local paper. The horse had only been roasted for half an hour due to impatience on the part of the borstal's chef, Slasher Simpkins, and so was only partially cooked. Every boy, girl and member of staff ate a plate of horse and all succumbed to the dastardly disease. They are all now on a course of high dose poultices and are being monitored around the clock by a specialist team of nuns from the local nunnery.

The Pollerang Beatings Centre, a vast complex on the eastern side of Central Pollerang, has been criticised by parents for being too lenient. The PBC was set up as a training facility for children aged 5-20 years as a means of beating some sense into them rather than sending them to a normal school. All core subjects come complete with particular beatings. This method has been proven by scientific testing to make children a lot more receptive to learning. For example, students learning English are punched in the stomach at the start of every lesson. Maths students are whipped every five minutes during lessons. Students learning sciences have half bricks thrown at them randomly throughout the lesson. One of the most popular courses is Languages. Pupils studying French or German are thumped on the back of the head with a mallet every eleven minutes, while students learning Hebrew and Tagalog are repeatedly electrocuted with varying voltages, depending on their performance. Parents are concerned that the regime at the Centre is not strict enough. One of the worried parents, 59 year-old Tony Megabird, father of Fantasia Megabird, 12, studying English and Tagalog, thinks that his daughter being punched and electrocuted on a daily basis is simply not enough. *"What about being stabbed, shot, thrown down stairs or attacked by wild animals?"* he said yesterday with an unsettling manic glee.

Goriton's new Delinquent Academy, which opened only six months ago, is proving to be an outstanding success. The Governor of the Academy, Sir Malcolm Uterine-Cavity is delighted with results so far and hopes to continue in the same vein. Sir Malcolm was drafted in to take over the Academy when the previous Governor dramatically resigned after being put in a large tank and boiled by some students taking a course in rudimentary witchcraft and soup making. Due to the relaxed attitude at the facility, inmates could more or less do what they liked. A new, much harsher regime was put in place by Sir Malcolm. His approach was to show each new inmate the view from the 20th floor of the Academy before tightly rolling them up in a carpet, setting it on fire and throwing it off the roof. The inmate would land a few seconds later on a series of boulders covered in broken glass. While admitting that this approach is low on rehabilitation, Sir Malcolm claims that none of his inmates have so far re-offended.

Classified Rancid Eggs for Sale

Is your urine not dark enough? Is your pee too pale? Then why not try our Urine Darkening Tablets. From hint of yellow to black tar, our pills will reinvigorate your trips to the water closet. Phone Yancey's Urine Enhancement Solutions on Western East Buntyside 03.

Wisdom teeth for hire. All sizes and flavours. Specially grown at our Wisdom Teeth farm in dog's mouths. Enjoy crunching nuts, gobstoppers and ball bearings once again. Four quid each or two for four quid. Phone Glord 0000.

Bernard and Maureen Fistation are proud to announce the birth of their only child Pungo. Pungo was born at midnight last night and weighed in at ten stone three pounds, with a height of five and half feet. He can walk already and this morning he went out for the paper. He is the second largest child to be born at Gubbenstery Maternity Unit this week.

Bovine Mortification Supplies proudly announces the arrival of new season Cow Vanity Blankets. Provide the dignity that all cows deserve by obscuring their latest meadow muffin. Next time your favourite cow drops a steamer simply reach for the CVB and spare any embarrassment for the animal. Call Clifford for a quote on Southern Gubbenstery 0101.

Inconsiderate and irritable large deafening woman requires smallish man for verbal onslaught. Must be available in the morning for relentless tirades about this and that and twice in the evening for protracted periods of haranguing. Apply in writing to Big Beverly Smonce, Monstrous Mansion House, Grotesque Gardens, Gubbenstery.

Bad-tempered cat for sale. Answers to the name of Fuckypoos. Phone Billy Bip now. Comes with own bowl, blanket and library card.

Now Open!

The New Restaurant by Celebrated French Chef Marcel Malaise

L'Enorme Estomac

Starters
Pickled Ox in Tub
Spicy Raw Wild Animal Meat Encased in Frozen Mutton
(Vegetarian)
Slab of Butter in Pork Sauce
Monkey Ribs Sweetened in Home-Made Cuckoo Sauce
Acidic Beef in Brown Yoghurt
Arabian Frog Noodles in Molten Pig Oil Dressing
Oriental Swedish Worm Bomb
Golden Chicken Ground to Dust *(Serves 2)*
Crispy Soup in Horsemeat Jelly *(Hot!)*
Small Mouse in Brine *(Unusually filling!)*

Mains
Contempt of Duck
*Whole duck burst open in boiling suet, garnished with beak, paws and gizzard
and drizzled with succulent buzzing relish*

Stagnate of Albino Venison Claw
*Whole deer claws roasted alive in bright milk and served with wood pulp and
full box of salt*

Dodecahedron of Mixed Poultry
*Some sort of bird frozen solid and sliced with a buzz saw at your table and
bathed in a zesty pulped vapour*

Compendium of Clay Pigeon (Vegetarian)
*The finest hand-reared clay pigeon served in a gobbis with gibbon milk, dog
antler patē and two slices of nutball*

Assemblage of Terrine of Mignon
*Freshly caught and hammered terrine, baked with mignon cubes and served
with a full glass of peppermint lard*

Roast Whole Wasp
Nineteen whole wasps oven-broiled in monkey oil and gnat's throat fluid and served with roast potatoes, chips, potato waffle, mashed potato and minced otter syrup

Sweets

Mippy Loar
Tangy goat biscuits in reeking custard with papaya lardons

Skaag Boop
Whole watermelons (6) in nutty ripe egg roulade topped with pepper gas

Dontis Pizenny
Free-range grease cake floating in lukewarm vinegar

Glatty
Vaporized honey with dog biscuits and blackcurrant steam

Yekky Doris
Lamb kebabs in crude cake with linseed of strawberry piffle

Scunto Dreezle
Cat bones in greyhound kidney sauce with powdered beanegg scrubbles

Side Orders	Drinks
Unnamed Vegetables	Bovril
English Corned Beef	Dog Oil
More Dog Biscuits	Salt Water
Dog Ear Crisps	Bladder Oil
Vulture Broth	Onion Cider
Frozen Chips	Oil of Cloves
Cock Niblets	Opaque Liquid
Nippy Buns	Fresh Potato Juice
Can of Milk	Hidenorhair Soup
Cigarettes	Liquefied Monkey
Putty	Evaporated Whisky

Prices of seasonal dishes may vary, i.e. get more expensive. Please ask at reception for special key to secret door at back. Open the door and go in. Wait to be seated. Ask the third woman from the left for a menu. Ask the fourth woman from the left for a menu with prices. Make your way to the apiary. Select a bee. Wait to be seated.

L'Enorme Estomac, 23 Queezian Street, Gubbenstery.

Sports News

Calamity at the Gubbenstery Athletics Meeting

By our athletics editor *Baby-Doc Mahogany*

The prestigious annual Gubbenstery Athletics Meeting ended in disarray yesterday after a series of unusual incidents took place. Most of the events seemed to be blighted by some mishap or other. Even though the day did not run according to plan, the 100,000 capacity crowd seemed to enjoy the spectacle. The opening event, the men's 100 metres, set the standard for the rest of the day. Two of the competitors arrived with an incomplete running kit due to a robbery at their hotel. Chester Heepees of Iceland arrived with no running shoes and had to borrow a pair of hobnail boots from one of the greenkeepers and Percy Jillaroid from Germany arrived with no shorts or underpants and had to run with his genitalia exposed. When the gun went, all eight runners flew out of the blocks at speed and all went well until the halfway point. Suddenly, one of Heepees' boots came off and smashed the favourite, Gumpy McAlister of Taiwan, in the mouth knocking several teeth out. McAlister hit the deck and two of the other runners fell over him, one receiving a broken thumb and the other dislocating both hips. Thirty metres from the finish, Jillaroid dived for the line and flew through the air like an obese swan. At the finish it was a dead heat between Chester Heepees and the Chinese competitor Larry Conko. Jillaroid landed behind the first two and suffered 99% abrasion burns after landing on the rough running surface. The gold medal was awarded to Heepees by one hundred trillionth of a microsecond and Conko stormed off in a huff, swearing in Chinese as he went.

In the women's 100 metres, there was fierce rivalry between the two hot favourites for the gold medal, Nancy Varbonate of Northern Israel and Beverly Acetate from Southern Israel. The pair had traded insults prior to yesterday's race. Varbonate had called Acetate a stinking ball of lard and Acetate had referred to Varbonate as a flabby fuckhead. The feuding sprinters were drawn next to each other in lanes 4 and 5 and did not look at each other during the warm up. When the gun went, Varbonate threw a punch at Acetate, catching her in the central groin area. Acetate retaliated by lunging forward and biting a hole in Varbonate's cheek. The other athletes took off at speed and raced away from the squabbling pair. At 50 metres, all eight women were in a line and running at top speed. Suddenly, Varbonate pulled a knife out of her shorts and slashed Acetate on the legs and face. Acetate screamed in pain but managed to grab her pistol from her knickers holster. She fired two shots at Varbonate, shooting off both her breasts. It was Varbonate's turn to scream in agony. The bickering sprinters launched an all-out attack on each other at the 70-metre mark as the other women ran on. On the finish line, the remaining six women were all given the same time and all received a gold medal. Stewards had to intervene to break up the altercation between Varbonate and Acetate. Both women were taken away on stretchers with a multitude of stab wounds, gunshot wounds and a localised outbreak of scabies.

The men's 110-metre hurdles was a much anticipated event with the big clash being between Gubbenstery's very own Walter Birdbrain and the American Clint Steeroid. Throughout the year, the two of them had been setting world records so this was the clash everyone was looking forward to. The two great runners appeared to be on friendly terms despite their rivalry. They were sitting chatting to each other on the blocks and Birdbrain was enjoying his usual pre-race cigarette. Steeroid was chowing down on his customary pre-race triple cheese burger, large fries and litre of coffee. With the pleasantries over, the athletes lined up and the starter fired the gun. The official starting gun had malfunctioned in an earlier heat and the starter was using his own Smith and Wesson 500 handgun to start the race. Unfortunately, the starter wasn't watching where he was aiming and he blew the athletes in lanes 1, 2 and 3 to smithereens. Also, an 80 year-old mum-of-one and her pet cat sitting in the stadium were slaughtered by an unlucky ricochet of the heavy calibre bullet. When the officials had cleaned up the area, the athletes once again lined up and the gun was fired. As the hurdlers took off at speed, a swan passing overhead was blown to pieces by the starter's pistol and the beautiful white feathers fell to the ground like blood-spattered snowflakes. The great rivals were neck and neck at halfway, a full 5 metres ahead of what was left of the field. As the two great competitors leapt over the ninth hurdle, Steeroid's stomach burst open, dispersing his innards across the track. Steeroid crashed to the floor and Birdbrain slipped on Steeroid's jejunum and also hit the deck, fracturing his forehead in the process. The competitor from North Korea, Stig Olafson, in the outside lane, was untroubled by the pandemonium and sprinted home in the leisurely time of 15 seconds. Far from a world record, but still a gold medal.

In the women's discus final, the hot favourite for gold, Chastity Plonce of Japan, was having a nightmare. Her first two attempts were 48.2 metres and 51.1 metres, well below her personal best of 75.5 metres and she was languishing in tenth position. On her final attempt, she entered the circle and prepared to throw. Just as she was winding up her throw, a hornet landed on her and stung her on the pancreas. A massive jolt of pain shot through her body causing her to launch the discus at an incredible speed. The 1kg lenticular disc flew through the air and landed in the main stand at the opposite end of the stadium. Unfortunately, it became lodged in the mouth of a large gentleman. Plonce's throw was quickly measured before the large man spat it out and it was a colossal new world record of 151 metres. Her mighty hornet-induced throw gave her a fifth gold medal and a hero's homecoming to look forward to back in Yokohama.

In the closing stages of the men's 50km walk, the rank outsider from the Faroe Islands, Galaroy Pompazian, had a lead of over 20km when he entered the stadium. The crowd went wild as the underrated hoofer from the east end of Kirkjubøur seemed destined to collect his country's first ever gold medal. However, it was not to be as the cruel hand of fate dealt a dreadful blow. As Pompazian entered the home straight to complete the last 100 metres of his gruelling hike, both his legs became detached at the hip and fell off. The crowd gasped, as did Pompazian. He crumpled in a heap and was overtaken 90 minutes later by the entire field, with the gold medal going to Raymond Dildoe of Vietnam.

Many of the events were blighted by unusual occurrences which seemed to add to the spectacle of a great day's athletics. Even one of the medal ceremonies resulted in mayhem. As Winifred Lokup-Garrage of Guatemala stepped up to get her gold medal for winning the women's 1.5 metre dash, the podium gave way and she fell through and disappeared down an uncovered manhole. She was trapped down in the bowels of the stadium for 3 hours before being rescued by a trained rescue goat. Fortunately, she only sustained two broken legs, two dislocated buttocks and a minor outbreak of rabies in one of her eyes, after ingesting over 20 litres of raw sewage.

Despite the odd mishap here and there, Gubbenstery's big day of athletics was judged a roaring success and plans are already afoot to increase the capacity of the stadium to 800,000, such is the demand for next year's event.

The Legend that is

Agnes Bowhandle of the Wild West

By our gory crime correspondent *Albert Bubbo*

Agnes Bowhandle was born in 1849 in Tombstone, Arizona. Her parents were local prostitute Dolores Bowhandle and a drifter called Floyd Lonesome. She never knew her father and was raised by her mother in her place of work, The Carnal Rooms Brothel. At the age of five Agnes killed her first man. A dissatisfied cowboy was beating up her mother when Agnes took matters into her own hands. She ran at the cowboy and launched herself feet first through the air and lodged herself in the cowboy's mouth up to her hips. She then pushed her feet down his throat and bit off his nose. After fourteen hours in this position the cowboy choked to death and Agnes was given a stern telling off by the local magistrate.

At the age of six Agnes killed her second man and strangely enough, it was the local magistrate. He had questioned the change he got from a ten dollar bill and Agnes saw this as a sign of disrespect. She ran next door to the blacksmiths and grabbed his anvil and sprinted back to the brothel at incredible speed and launched the anvil straight at the magistrate and it lodged part way down his gullet. As the magistrate struggled to adapt to having an anvil in his mouth, Agnes grabbed her mother's wood chopping axe and sliced off the magistrates arms and legs and filled his nostrils with pepper. Dolores Bowhandle tried to calm her daughter but Agnes had lost her temper big time. She snatched up the resident brothel dog, George Cooper, and rammed him into her mother's mouth, before turning her rage back to the magistrate. He was lying helpless in a pool of blood but Agnes wasn't satisfied. Her bloodlust was fired up and she looked around for another weapon. She grabbed a bottle of moonshine whiskey from the mantelpiece and drank about half of it in one gulp. The rest she poured over the magistrate and set him alight, occasionally stoking the fire with his arms and legs. By the time the sheriff arrived, the magistrate was charcoal and Agnes's mother had accidentally swallowed the dog. The new magistrate gave Agnes a severe talking to and ordered her to stay in her bedroom for ten years.

When Agnes was sixteen she came out her room and she was a very different prospect to the helpless little girl that had entered the room ten years earlier. She was now six feet tall and massively robust. She had thighs like a man's waist, arms like a man's thigh, and hands like industrial shovels. Her long blond hair had remained uncut and was now up in a three foot beehive style and she was wearing six inch stiletto heels, giving her a total height of nine and a half feet. She became the resident enforcer in the brothel with the sole purpose of keeping the punters in line. She kept two six-shooters on her hip for any particularly nasty trouble, but seldom resorted to gunfire. Agnes managed to keep the customers under control using alternative methods.

On Agnes's twentieth birthday, she was sitting relaxing at a table at the back of the brothel with her usual pint of whiskey and cigar when in walked a stranger. He went to reception and ordered a woman. Doris, the head girl, said she would service him and the two disappeared into one of the bedrooms. Ten minutes later loud screams came from the bedroom and Agnes knew it was her responsibility to investigate. She ran along the corridor and kicked the bedroom door off its hinges. Inside, the stranger had tied up Doris with piano wire and forced a pillow into her mouth as he attempted to have his wicked way with her. Agnes immediately sprang into action. She picked the man up by the hair and started spinning him round her head, then threw him against the wall. She pounced on him and sat on his chest. She then thrust her whole hand into the man's mouth, down his throat and pulled his stomach out of his mouth and ate it. The unknown man begged for mercy but Agnes was relentless. She punched and kicked him for a while and then she reached for her rope and plunged it down the man's throat and out of his anus. She then lifted him up by the rope and hung him from a roof beam. Doris thanked Agnes and made her way back to reception. Only the unwary stepped out of line in The Carnal Rooms, and they didn't do it twice.

Agnes was an attractive woman and occasionally turned a few tricks of her own when she wanted some extra money, but only the most reckless, wicked or ill-informed men would consider a session with Agnes. As long as she had her pints of whiskey, her cigars and the occasional bout of deranged intercourse, Agnes was more or less well behaved. However, when Agnes was twenty five, and at the peak of her muscular and sexual powers, she fell in love. Her lover was the new sheriff, Leroy Maddox. Leroy had arrived from Abilene, Texas, as a replacement for the previous sheriff Mr Rubenstein who had been eaten by wolves. Agnes fell in love with Leroy in a matter of minutes and Leroy reciprocated.

All went well for Agnes and Leroy and they attended many cheese and wine parties and weekend trips to the greyhound racing. They became the town's premiere couple and life couldn't be better for Tombstone's number one enforcer of the law, and Leroy. Alas, this period of tranquillity was not to last. On a sunny July afternoon the notorious Penguin brothers, Jake, 20, Rowdy, 30, and Monty, 70, rode into town looking for trouble. They went to the Holy Mackerel Bar and starting drinking and gambling and causing a general ruckus. One thing led to another and eventually a fight broke out, resulting in Jake shooting a man dead. The bar owner ran out and told Leroy what had happened and he immediately made his way to the bar. As he pushed through the double saloon doors, he was met by a hail of bullets from the Penguin brothers and was cut to pieces.

One of the waitresses ran to Agnes's house and told her the news. A fearsome look appeared in Agnes's eyes and she broke the waitress's nose and jaw with one savage punch simply for bringing the bad news. She took off her guns and strode purposefully over to the bar with a rage simmering within her. She stepped over Leroy's body and entered the bar. Everyone had left except the Penguin brothers, who were still gulping down whiskey and playing cards. Agnes asked who shot Leroy and Jake said it was him, as he finished another bottle of whiskey. Agnes walked over to Jake and punched him so hard on the nose that her fist went right through his head and out the other side. She then picked him up and threw him out through the window and he landed about 20 yards down the street. Rowdy reached for his rifle but Agnes grabbed it first and rammed it down his throat and pulled the trigger. Both barrels went off and blew a massive hole in his lower stomach. She fired it again and blew his feet off before picking up the piano and dropping it on his head. As Monty made a move to run out of the door, Agnes grabbed him by the throat and bit into his forehead, removing a large chunk of head. She then pulled out her samurai sword from her belt and drove it into Monty's stomach, before pulling out all his intestines and suspending him from the rafters with his own guts. She pulled back her sword ready to deliver the coup de grâce, when Monty spoke. *"Don't do it Agnes,"* he said. *"My name's not really Monty Penguin." "Who are you then?"* asked Agnes. *"The name's Lonesome, Floyd Lonesome. I'm your dad Agnes." "I don't have a dad,"* said Agnes, as she swung her sword and sliced her father in two, right down the middle. With blood and entrails and bits and bobs of her dad scattered around her feet, Agnes roared loudly, *"I'm the new sheriff in town and I'm going to clean up this shithole"*.

Women's Classified Products

Large supply of offensive swear words left over following a savage argument with the Missus. Mainly words beginning with F and C and one beginning with W. Write to Frank Slaughter at Kybosh House, Poiko Road, Gubbenstery.

Adorable bulldog puppy for sale. Not house trained so may eat TV and bite visitors. Also acts as an alarm clock by incessant hourly barking through the night. For a free trial with Snappy the dog send £158 to Iris Boyong, No. 6 Nappy Valley, Glord.

Second hand full size model of a pair of scissors for sale. Comes with a full service history and a year's supply of dairy cattle. Contact Delbert Ronky, Flat 0, Nuzzian Street, Gubbenstery any evening after sundown.

Missing cat for sale. Answers to the name of Funko the cat. Call Tabitha Spagboll on Glord 0101 for all the latest updates and a reading of the complete Bible in Icelandic.

Glord Farmer's Market
Every second Tuesday at the start of the month and every third Tuesday at the end of the month. Simply turn up and fill your car with bargains such as two for one mice, pumpkins carved into the shape of a lavatory cistern and much, much more. Free parking for all mustard coloured five-wheel cars on a Tuesday evening. Glong Industrial Estate, Glord.

English corned beef rear bumpers, steering wheels, roof racks and spare wheels on sale at Handy Andy McPandy's all natural car spares. No artificial flavourings used. Free English corned beef-scented furry dice for every customer with a broken leg. 16 Functionality Street, Glord.

Volunteers needed for church fete on the 25th. Experience of cakes, wine making, adult sex games and voodoo would be an advantage. Contact the vicar (Heehaw McVicar) at Gurbanoid Elementary Church of Whoopee, Kinawful Road, Gubbenstery.

Bob Leopard and Cynthia Pompo
Live at
The Gubbenstery Pavilion

By our thaumaturge reporter *Randolph Donkeyman*

Continuing their smash hit world tour, world famous magician Bob Leopard and his glamorous assistant Cynthia Pompo put on a spectacular show at the GP last night. The arena was packed to the rafters to welcome one of the world's most unorthodox magicians and entertainers and the audience were hoping for something special. They were not disappointed. Bob took to the stage wearing an all-in-one black jump suit with Cynthia at his side wearing an all-in-one black bra.

Bob opened the show by throwing a coconut at high speed all the way to the back of the hall, bouncing it off a bald man's head and catching it again. The whole audience gasped, especially the man struck by the coconut. He then clapped his hands together releasing a large puff of white smoke and instantly a porcupine and a wombat fell from the ceiling, landing on spectators in the front row. This caused chaos as some people were bitten and others jabbed by sharp spines. The rest of the audience clapped and cheered wildly. He then selected a member of the audience to join him and Cynthia on stage and asked the chap to run as fast as he could from one side of the stage to the other and jump through the mystical mirror into a magical world beyond. A short man with a huge beer gut did as he was told and sprinted like a startled gazelle straight at the mirror. He crashed into it with incredible force, lacerating himself badly and showering the audience with glass splinters. Bob burst into laughter and said he did that stunt every night to see just what you could make stupid people do.

After the ambulance left, Cynthia selected another person from the crowd to take part in the next trick. The woman selected was given a high velocity rifle and told that if she could open a special box by shooting the padlock off, she would win £5. The woman lay on the stage and took aim at a box that had descended from the rafters and hung about four feet above the heads of the audience. The crowd hushed and the woman lay motionless with her finger on the trigger. All of a sudden she fired and a deafening bang reverberated around the auditorium, bursting eardrums as it went, and the padlock flew off the box. She had done it. The £5 was hers. As the padlock fell to the ground and the door of the box opened, thousands of hornets and horseflies were released into the auditorium, stinging and biting their way through the audience. This heralded the end of the first half of a thrilling show.

Following a twenty minute interval to allow medical treatment for stings, bites, jabs and assorted open wounds, the crowd were soon back in their seats and full of expectation. Bob returned to the stage wearing only a tartan bra and knickers. Cynthia was right behind him riding a goat and wearing only tartan boxer shorts. This time Bob replaced his opening coconut trick with a heavy iron soup ladle which he immediately threw straight at the upper circle. It hit a middle aged woman flush on the mouth, knocking half her teeth out and yet somehow returned boomerang-like straight into Bob's hand. The audience gasped with appreciation and the toothless woman gasped in pain. Cynthia then leapt off the goat and landed on Bob's shoulders. In a flash, Bob applied high voltage electrodes to the goat's ears and gave it the full juice from a car battery. The goat flipped onto its back and began squirting milk all over the audience from its udders, before jumping to its feet and sprinting off stage at speed. The spectators loved it. More, more, more they shouted, and Bob obliged.

He loaded Cynthia into a large catapult-like contraption and fired her right up into the dark, high above the crowd. Cynthia did not come down. It appeared as if she had magically vanished and the crowd started muttering amongst themselves. About a minute later there was a deafening bang and bright flash from far above the audience. All of a sudden and from seemingly out of nowhere, Cynthia was descending rapidly, but she was not alone. She was on the back of a hyena which in turn was on the back of a rhinoceros and all three were plummeting downwards at breakneck speed. The threesome landed with a loud crash on a group of people in the middle of the crowd, breaking bones and fracturing skulls. Cynthia nipped the ear of the hyena with pliers, which in turn bit the neck of the rhino causing it to gallop onto the stage and stand next to Bob. Cynthia jumped off her mammalian taxi and the crowd delivered more thunderous applause.

Bob then amused the audience with some close up conjuring and sleight of hand using boiling hot ball bearings, hypodermic needles and scorpions. He then invited a man in his twenties on stage and blindfolded him. He threaded a rope in one nostril, up his nose and down the other nostril. One end of the rope disappeared off to the side and the other end was hooked up to a high speed winch. Bob flipped a switch and the winch pulled in the rope at colossal speed, burning the man's nasal septum, until a large anvil was revealed at the other end of the rope racing across the stage. The anvil whizzed through the air and clattered the man on the nose, knocking him senseless for a few minutes. When he awoke, he was being rewarded with rapturous applause as he was being loaded into a large tank of water with a stun grenade floating in it. The lid was locked onto the top of the tank and there appeared to be no way out for the chap. But indeed there was. As the fellow began to drown in the tank, the stun grenade exploded and shattered all the glass, safely delivering the man onto the floor of the stage exhausted, deafened and cut to pieces. By this time, the crowd were standing on their seats and begging Bob for more.

Bob said he was about to perform his final trick of the evening and could the crowd please be quiet. A large curtain was then raised to reveal Bob standing next to a canon pointing at a greyhound about forty feet away and Cynthia crouching behind the dog. Bob lit the fuse on the canon and counted down 3, 2, 1. All of a sudden, the canon went off with a massive, eardrum-splintering bang and fired a mallard duck headfirst straight at the greyhound. The duck flew straight in the dog's agape mouth, went right through it, and came blasting out of its arsehole, to be caught in a bucket by Cynthia, who triumphantly held it aloft. The greyhound appeared to stagger off stage with a slight limp, before Bob and Cynthia took a standing ovation from the crowd. As a final treat, the master magician, as if by magic, produced two high-powered airguns from Cynthia's boxer shorts and the magical duo starting firing lead pellets at the audience as they left the auditorium. As the delighted audience wiped blood from heads, ears and noses, every one of them headed straight for the booking office to pre-book tickets for Bob and Cynthia's next performance.

For the greatest day of your life
Visit
Alcoholand

By our hard liquor correspondent *Spongo Nelson*

"The greatest theme park the world has ever known." That's the proud boast of the owner of Alcoholand, Mr Bernard Spunkate. I was invited by Mr Spunkate to sample the delights of Alcoholand and to see if it lived up to all the hype. Alcoholand has been consistently voted the number one theme park in Gubbenstery and surrounding area every year since it opened five years ago. Other popular theme parks such as Wormland, Fountain Pen World and Jaundice World have all been playing catch up to the ever popular juggernaut that is Alcoholand. I arrived bright and early at 5am at the vast expanse of Alcoholand and was met at one of the many turnstiles by Mr Spunkate himself. He greeted me with a broad smile, like someone who was mentally insane. He ushered me through the turnstile, only charging me the midweek off-peak rate of £109.19 entrance fee. There was no one else here so I had the whole theme park to myself.

We approached the first attraction called *Drinkypoos* and I was instructed by the smiling young lady to drink the pint of green liquid she handed me. I asked what it was but she said it was a secret recipe. As I brought it to my mouth, the stench raced up my nose and nearly made me pass out. It took me about a minute to gulp it down. Immediately, the lining of my nose started to burn, my tongue went numb and my eyes were watering like Niagara Falls. My legs were jelly-like but I was happy to still be standing. From out of nowhere the young lady swung a massive rubber hammer and caught me a meaty blow right on the nose and knocked me to the ground. As I lay there, she managed to thud in another ten big hits right onto my nose until it went numb and I was seeing stars. All this time Bernard Spunkate was laughing his head off. He then helped me up and said all I had to do now to complete the first session was to eat the whole raw conger eel. As I chewed down the last mouthful of the truly repugnant slimy eel, the girl unleashed her massive hammer and again she targeted my nose. After another massive battering and a complete emptying of my stomach contents, Spunkate dragged me to my feet and said well done. He then took £20 off me and explained that the £109.19 was only an entrance fee. All the attractions and rides in the park had to be paid for separately. My head was feeling a bit woozy with whatever alcohol was in the vile green drink and my nose had been flattened and drained of all its blood.

Spunkate then led me to the next treat, which appeared to be some sort of rollercoaster called *The Ethanol Express*. We boarded the front car and were strapped in. Immediately, a man appeared and I was fitted with a plastic face mask with a long tube leading off it to a large funnel. He then poured in a bottle of whisky which I had no choice but to gulp down. It burned my throat and my head started to spin. He then poured in a bottle of Campari, a bottle of Advocaat and a litre of Pummelhead English fortified wine in quick succession. I nearly vomited up my lower intestine and it felt like there was a rhinoceros loose inside my skull but I managed to drink the lot. Again, Spunkate was sitting next to me laughing like a mental case. Suddenly, the roller coaster took off at high speed and went round a series of stomach-churning loops and then crashed through a large tank of boiling melted butter, before starting a steep climb to the top of a 300-foot tower. I was now soaked in rancid butter and it felt awful. At the top of the tower the roller coaster suddenly plummeted at great speed and as we hurtled towards the ground, high voltage electric shocks started coming through my seat. This caused my legs to straighten violently and made me leap out of the roller coaster at about 150 feet in the air. My extreme drunkenness was immediately cured as I flew through the air. I crashed into a large tank of water containing piranha fish and they nearly had my fingers chewed to the bone before I escaped. Spunkate then turned up, again laughing like a wild man. He said it was time to move on to the next event.

We entered a dimly lit hut called *The Pulverizing Bin* which contained a bar complete with barman. He served me some foul-tasting cocktails and some shots of absolute ethanol until I began to feel my whole body go numb. He then grabbed me and put me inside an old metal dustbin and locked the lid shut. Only then did I find out there was also a wasp's nest inside the dustbin and the wasps were even less pleased than I was about being in there. Something started bashing the bin relentlessly, before turning it upside down. Suddenly the lid opened and me and the wasps were emptied onto a huge water slide which we slid down at breakneck speed before being brought to a sudden halt by the concrete blocks at the bottom. I was stung all over, my nose was bleeding again and one of my ears was missing. You-know-who was standing there howling with laughter. I was a very annoyed, semi-drunk, buttery mess and I gave Spunkate a telling off. He suggested we move to the next item.

He led me into a booth where I was grabbed by two burly men who fitted me with a square glass helmet and fixed me to some sort of revolving contraption. I was told that this was called The *Helmet of Fuck* and the helmet would be topped up with various drinks and the only way I could breathe would be to drink the drinks first. I started to complain but was kicked in the scrotum and punched in the guts a few times. The helmet was then filled with vodka, which I gulped down to prevent suffocation. Subsequent top ups with brandy, Guinness, pig's blood and boiling gravy kept me busy trying to breathe while I was spun round at high speed. When I was let out, Spunkate was lying on the floor laughing. He said the best was still to come.

He ushered me into a lift which took us to the top of a 500-foot tower overlooking a barrel of vinegar far below. He then slipped a grenade on a chain over my neck and told me I had to undertake the final task, the legendary *Jump of Idiocy*. If I didn't jump off the tower into the barrel 500 feet below, the grenade would be detonated and blow my head off. Then came the usual extra nonsense. I had to drink a full bottle of alcohol before each jump and do it ten times. He then handed me a litre bottle of rum which I gulped down and vomited back up as I jumped off the tower. My aim was good and I landed in the barrel of vinegar with a tremendous thud. Back up I went and completed another nine jumps with various litre bottles of booze, except the last bottle, which was a five litre bottle of Jack Daniels. This impaired my judgement and I missed the barrel completely. I landed on top of a passing clown who was riding a horse. The clown was knocked out and the horse's legs splayed completely flat, but they both survived. Spunkate appeared but I could hardly focus on him. My eyesight was all over the place, my head was pounding, the skin was almost totally ripped off my legs from landing in that fucking barrel and my nose was a flattened, bleeding blob. I was also a bit deaf, had bitten through my tongue and was naked. Spunkate said I'd done well and gave me a lifetime free membership to Alcoholand. For anyone wishing to visit Alcoholand, be it on their own or with friends and family, I would say it's quite a challenge but it's very rewarding and would certainly be an ideal venue for all sorts of parties. Now I can see what all the fuss is about and why it's so popular. Incidentally, Mr Spunkate said he has plans to open a similar theme park for non-drinkers called Boiling Hot Porridge Land.

Outstanding Trouser Facilities

Highest quality Elimination Powder now on sale. Imported from somewhere near China. Ideal for household, industrial and abattoir uses. Available in 1 ounce or 1 ton easy open packs. Contact Inutile Industries on Glord 01.

Local spinster Miss Gladys Mushroob would like her many friends (gay and straight) to be aware that as from tomorrow night she will be changing her name to Miss Gladys Mushroomp for purposes of clarity and tax avoidance.

Exquisitely hand-crafted English corned beef footwear now available. Our stock includes gents' meaty moccasins and beefy brogues as well as ladies' high salt stilettos. Request our free catalogue for £3 per week or £4 per day.

Local unstable resident Desmond Glabberous would like to announce that he is about to burn his house down. Would his neighbours on either side kindly leave their own premises immediately. Your cooperation is appreciated.

Extra-large woman with vice-like grip available for hire. Reasonable hourly or yearly rates. Phone Clarissa Bonce at The Skiving Bastard pub on East Buntyside 666.

Individually hand-crafted exhaust fumes for the discerning gentleman. All sizes available in 10-ton cans. Ring Blippo for price and tide times. Gubbenstery 911.

East Buntyside Pig and Mountain Lion Research Unit

By our chief unreliable reporter *Dave Anthrax*

Information leaked from inside the tightly guarded walls of East Buntyside Pig and Mountain Lion Research Unit suggests some very strange goings-on indeed. My informant, who shall remain nameless, has told me some extraordinary stories involving the work that is being carried out behind the 50-foot high walled complex with razor wire and duck pond.

Originally, EBPAMLRU was set up to allow state-of-the-art experimental work to be performed using animals, in an attempt to further medical sciences. However, the truth appears to be very different. My squealer has divulged some incredible information which can only be described as hair-raising. He or she tells me that on his or her first day in the lab they saw a door marked *No Entry*, which was slightly ajar. In the brief glimpse they had inside, they saw a poodle sitting smoking cigarettes at a table opposite what they can only describe as another dog that was smoking a pipe. The dogs appeared very relaxed and were playing black jack. At that point, someone inside slammed the door shut and my supergrass moved on. Another dog-related incident witnessed by my stool pigeon was equally shocking. They said there was a fenced off area at the back of the building and one day they had a look over the fence. Inside they saw what appeared to be a man innocently throwing a ball for a dachshund to chase. However, on closer inspection, they noticed the dachshund was actually two dachshunds joined together back to back with both sets of hind legs missing. The "double dog" was about 6 feet long with a head at both ends and two sets of front legs. Every time the ball was thrown, each front of dog would try to chase the ball resulting in a cruel but highly comic outcome.

As the months went by, my gossipmonger, who we'll call "he," began to notice more and more odd goings-on. On one occasion, he was going to an area of the complex he hadn't been to before. En route he passed a huge glass window which revealed a completely white room and inside he saw a cat chasing a mouse. Nothing odd about that, but in this case the cat had been fitted with the wings from a goose and the mouse had been fitted with the wings of a sparrow. The mouse was whizzing around the room at lightning speed with the cat chasing it in a more laborious fashion due to its much bigger wing span. On another occasion, my blabbermouth went down to the basement for the first time and saw a door marked *The Bowling Ball Men*. When he looked in he saw four men playing some sort of bizarre sport on a basketball court. The unusual thing was that each of the men were naked and he could clearly see that both the feet and both the buttocks of each man had been replaced by bowling balls and they were careering around the court at incredible speeds chasing a hockey puck. He wasn't sure of the rules of the game or the score.

As my mouthpiece became more established at the EBPAMLRU, he, or Dr Norbert, as we shall call him, became more trusted by the bigwigs and gained access to more secretive areas of the facility. In the aquatic area, trials were underway with highly intelligent dolphins. Two of the brightest dolphins, Winnie and Beryl McAdam, had their mouths removed and replaced with the heads of Myah birds. This particular experiment had been set up at the behest of the Head of the facility, Professor Jim Zim, who was very keen to find out just how intelligent dolphins were. He said that because Myah birds could talk very well, they would be able to convey what the dolphins were thinking. As he put it, *"Let's see once and for all what these smartarse aquatic bastards have got to say for themselves".*

At this point in his career at the EBPAMLRU, my taleteller, or Dr Norbert Scryne, as we shall call him, had seen many strange and unsettling sights, although he did still believe that work at the centre was contributing to our greater understanding of scientific matters. Some well-established developments originating from the EBPAMLRU had actually become part of everyday life. For instance, the subterranean mining kangaroo, the high-speed knitting octopus that operates the treadle loom used in the Harris Tweed industry, the valet parking baboons of North Hollywood and the elephants that go grocery shopping for house-bound people. All of these developments were benefits to society but most of what my loose-tongued fink told me seemed to be almost too strange for words.

One of the most startling discoveries made by my whistle-blowing snitch, although we'll call him Dr Norbert Scryne of 21 Putrescine Avenue, Tower Hamlets, London, is the way the projects are initially set up. According to my singing canary Dr Scryne, the scientists at the research unit simply sit around having cups of tea or whisky most of the time. They chat about most normal subjects such as the weather, football, transgender rugby matches and seeing who could throw a jackal the furthest. Suddenly, one of them would come up with a suggestion for a project. It didn't matter if there was any scientific benefit or if it was completely ludicrous. The project would go ahead.

In the past year alone, projects have been given the go ahead to explore such diverse topics as seeing how fast a man can run with a wheelbarrow full of bone china, the training of giraffes to be ridden across areas of quicksand, depriving a howler monkey of oxygen to see if this reduces its howling, the development of high strength automotive brakes which, when applied, can stop any car in twelve inches, no matter what speed it is doing, and many others. Dr Scryne claimed that even he was caught up in the whole fiasco and started putting forward project suggestions of his own. On one occasion, he decided to come up with such a preposterous idea that it would have to be rejected by the other scientists. He suggested a new type of sporting pastime where dwarves would race each other round a track on the back of dingoes and an equivalent version in a swimming pool with dwarves on the back of moray eels. To his astonishment, his nonsensical notion was given full backing by his head of department and a budget of £10,000,000. Trials of both versions of the sport are currently underway at The Nora Skunion Institute of Bastardisation in Texas.

Dr Scryne recently resigned his position as Head of Advanced Hosiery and Treacle Dynamics at EBPAMLRU and is currently undergoing intensive interrogation by most of the UK's police forces. It was during one period of particularly brutal interrogation at Police Headquarters in Port Saint Mary, Isle of Man that Dr Scryne came up with the idea of standard police issue boxing gloves to save wear and tear on officer's knuckles. Superintendent Yoko Boko of Thames Valley Police said that investigations would continue until the rugby season starts.

The Funny Farm

By our out and about reporter *Vera Mutance*

On the outskirts of Gubbenstery, near Stoolblood Lake, there is a secluded area that lies behind a 50-foot high wall. This is the Funny Farm. Established five years ago, the Funny Farm was the brainchild of retired veterinary surgeon Hugo Ratnage. According to Hugo, the Funny Farm was set up to educate the people of Gubbenstery and to let both adults and children alike interact with traditional farmyard animals. I was given a special guided tour by Hugo and encountered all of the inhabitants of the Funny Farm. In my own humble opinion, I don't think the animals I encountered are representative of animals that would be found in most farmyards. Hugo said that his animals may be slightly different to traditional farmyard animals but are more or less the same. I came to the Funny Farm expecting it to be a child-friendly petting zoo, but that was not the case.

As we left Hugo's office we were immediately met by two friendly-looking billy goats. Suddenly, one of the goats raced forward and head-butted me in the groin and knocked me over. As I hit the ground the other goat got on top of me and jumped up and down before peeing into my mouth. I leapt to my feet in a rage and pulled an ear off the peeing goat and punched the other one in the face. They ran off making a strange noise. I asked Hugo what that was all about and he said they were just being friendly. My host then suggested we visit the horse egg incubator and I thought he was joking. We entered a large greenhouse-like building and to my astonishment there were about twenty horses sitting on enormous eggs. The eggs were roughly the size of a beer barrel and each one had a horse lying on top of it. The heat in the horse incubator was ferocious and I could feel my brain frying. Hugo said the high temperature was to keep the horses docile and to stop them wandering off. He then took two hours to explain the workings of the horse incubator as I sweated out all my bodily fluids. I was trembling with heat stroke and was down to my bra and pants when I had to tell Hugo to shut the fuck up. At that point I fainted.

When I came to, I was outside the horse chamber lying on the ground and felt as if an atom bomb had been detonated quite close to my brain. It was then I noticed that Hugo had covered me in fresh, hot horse manure. He said he didn't want me to get cold before I had a chance to put my clothes back on. I told him I was fucking roasting and probably wouldn't cool down for another ten years but he seemed to laugh it off and suggested we continue with the tour. Before I had a chance to move I was set upon by hundreds of mice. They were crashing into me at incredible speeds and they seemed to create an utterly repugnant smell. Hugo explained that the mice were specially bred to produce copious amounts of a noxious gas in their intestines. They stored this gas until they were threatened when they would unleash it all in an instant out of their anus to power themselves away at up to 500mph. When I asked what the point of it was, he said it was so that the mice could avoid being eaten by cats. I suggested he would soon be overrun by stinking mice and he said that wouldn't be a problem. He told me the mice are regularly harvested, pulped and fed to the horses.

I got dressed and although I stank like a rotting corpse and had a headache that would kill a buffalo, I continued with the alleged tour. According to Hugo, our next stop was going to be a truly memorable experience for me. We entered a pen containing about ten large pigs. Hugo told me these were the Gumpigs. Since I wasn't in the best of moods, I asked him what the fuck a Gumpig was. Immediately Hugo blew a loud whistle and began scattering what looked like feed pellets on the ground. The pigs raced over and devoured all the pellets, although they did seem to be chewing for a long time. The pigs then settled down and just stood about. I told Hugo it wasn't a memorable experience but I was glad that the pigs were normal and I hadn't been attacked or peed on. At that point, Hugo gave three sharp blasts on his whistle, which by now was starting to annoy me. *"Shut that fucking whistle up,"* I told Hugo, and he just smiled. All of a sudden, there was a loud rumbling noise coming from the pigs and they became agitated. What I saw next completely overwhelmed my brain. The pigs started blowing bubble gum bubbles out of their rear ends and the bubbles kept getting bigger and bigger. Eventually the bubbles were the size of a small car and began to elevate the pig's hind quarters off the ground. A minute later the pigs were floating about ten feet above the ground in a tight hovering circle. They were right above my head when Hugo gave another three loud blasts of his fucking irritating whistle. I was just about to tell Hugo to shove his whistle deep into his arsehole when all of a sudden the pigs all started peeing. Somehow they all seemed to avoid Hugo but I was totally drenched in pig piss. *"What the fuck's going on here?"* I shouted at Hugo. He said he had bred the pigs to do this to avoid being eaten by wolves. I was so annoyed I jumped up to pull down one of the pigs to kick its head in but when I looked up, my mouth filled up with pig urine. This was the second time today I had copped a mouthful of farmyard pee. *"How the fuck is this of any use you stupid bastard?"* I said. He said the pigs were on the ground during the day and floated at night to avoid the wolves. When I told him there were no wolves in Gubbenstery he said it was in case they were reintroduced. I told him he had a screw loose and he just smiled.

I was about to leave when Hugo said there were still more lovely farmyard animals to see. Curiosity got the better of me so I traipsed on in my urine-saturated clothes. We reached a large pen and Hugo casually said this is where he keeps the ducks, geese, turkeys and pigeons. Sure enough the pen was full of such creatures but on closer inspection I noticed all the birds had four legs and were running around like small winged dogs with beaks. I asked Hugo what the point of this was and he said that when the birds were cooked, four legs were better than two. When I suggested that these unfortunate creatures were not ducks or turkeys any more he said it didn't matter. They were going in the oven anyway so you could call them what you like. Over the next hour Hugo, in his infinite madness, showed me donkeys that dig tunnels, to avoid sunstroke, sheep that only eat dead birds to recycle dead birds, and rabbits that have been bred to have the mouth of an Alsatian, for guarding premises. One of the bastard rabbits had a go at my hand and nearly bit my thumb off. I managed to punch it hard on the nose and knocked it out. Hugo's final presentation was to show me a large cage full of hens. I asked him if the hens were venomous or had rabies or some other fucking ludicrous scenario. He said they were perfectly normal and we could go in the cage and see them. The first minute in the cage was normal with the hens fucking about squawking. Unannounced, Hugo blew his bastard whistle and the hens took off into the air and flapped about just above my head. Suddenly they all laid eggs and they rained down on me like boulders and smashed onto my skull. I was pulverised by about 20 eggs and was in a right state. I'd had enough. I grabbed Hugo's whistle and stuck it in his forehead. As he winced I smashed him in the balls with the palm of my hand and he hit the floor. I told him he was a fucking idiot and should be locked up. Before I left, I broke both his ankles by jumping on them and stormed off. As I left, Hugo shouted at me. *"Don't go. You haven't seen the two-legged cow that drives the tractor yet."*

Activities for the Young at Heart

Enjoy the full benefits of tripe by ordering some tripe from The British Tripe Institute, 77 Goiloi Street, Valve of Morgagni, Italy.

Man obsessed with breathing in steam seeks similarly stupid person for steam nights and afternoons enjoying flavoured roasted water vapour.
Email: daftbastard@thick.dullard

Good home required for otter, seal and beaver. Reluctantly offloading my three pets due to a sum of money going missing, leading to a disagreement with all three. All are fully house trained and are able to make cheese on toast, darn socks and perform light housework. Phone Miss Gorpo McAlpine on Scrutto 3333.

Why not try Uncle Medwyn's new style sugar trousers. 28 – 48 inch waist available. Liquorice belts and spaghetti braces now 2 for the price of 2.

Learn Basic Home Surgery. We will teach you how to deal with most non-serious ailments such as in-growing toenail, dart through eye, missing kneecaps, asymmetric ears, gall bladder transplant and underarm itch. Phone Professor Barry Midgut now for free telephone-based tuition at £1 per hour + another £10 per hour as well.

Cat with own torch seeks dog with own car for night-time camping trips. Phone Tigger Tarbuck at the East Buntyside String Factory.

Black market monkey eggs for sale. Email Rick Spronce at rsgibbon@ apeshit.chimp.

Wide range of small electronic club feet for sale or hire. Contact Peter Scoliosis at the head office or Craig Narlarly at Bendy Simon's Yoga Club.

Now Open to the Public
Gubbenstery Castle

The newly restored Gubbenstery Castle is now open to the public and offers a great day out for the whole family. The castle has been fully restored over a period of eighteen years by the renowned historian Dr Scronto Blorian and his wife Dotty. Scronto and Dotty have worked tirelessly to rebuild the magnificent castle, a project that at first seemed impossible, considering they started with one remaining brick of the original castle. The restored castle is now over a mile long and sixteen storeys high, complete with half mile high walls, central courtyard, spring-loaded drawbridge and three mile deep moat. The castle and surrounding grounds offer many sports, events and pastimes to suit people of all mental aptitudes.

Tree Jumping

The castle grounds contain over a hundred magnificent Scots pine trees, some of which are over 2,000 feet tall. A few of the tallest trees have been adapted for people to make the two hour climb up to the observation basket at the top and enjoy the magnificent views over Gubbenstery and the surrounding area. The return trip down to the ground takes a mere ten seconds as you leap out over the upper leaf canopy and plummet at over 100mph towards the super high tension trampoline situated below, which safely breaks your fall. Enjoy the dramatically high bounce off the trampoline as you soar through the air with all the freedom of a large flightless bird. Eventually you will land somewhere in the grounds, hopefully with your knees bent to absorb the high impact. An unforgettable experience.

Birds of Prey

Enjoy an encounter with some of the world's most fearsome aerial predators as our Master falconer Ernie Yoopis introduces you to the ostrich, swan, albatross and goggle-eyed vulture, to name but a few. You will have the opportunity to jump from our highest trees with a marabou stork on each foot and an emu on each shoulder. Imagine the exhilaration of flying through the air at speed and enjoy the sight of the rapidly approaching ground as you and your new bird friends squawk and screech with fear. An unusual and exciting experience.

Archery

Gasp at the brilliance and partial accuracy of our top archers as they fire their mediaeval arrows with razor sharp points at targets over ten feet away. Our archers are handpicked from Gubbenstery's prisons and trained for over an hour in the ways of the bow and arrow. You will be firmly bound using razor wire to a revolving target made of hay which will then be spun by a tractor engine at over 5,000rpm. The archers will then fire 100 arrows at you and hope to hit the areas of the target made of hay. You will be amazed at the excitement you can generate as you watch the deadly arrows hurtling towards you. An experience not to be forgotten.

Drawbridge Trips

Maximize the thrills of a castle visit by partaking of a drawbridge trip. You will be fully fitted with our heavy wooden gliding wings and strapped into the special drawbridge firing chair. The drawbridge will be wound back until the heavy duty springs are loaded with maximum torque. Our expert will set fire to the restraining rope and you will be able to watch it slowly burn right through. Suddenly and without warning the rope will snap, thereby releasing the huge spring mechanism and you will be hurtled skywards at over 300mph. At maximum altitude (around 5-6,000 feet) it will then be up to you to release yourself from the firing chair, adjust the wooden gliding wings for optimal aeronautical manoeuvrability and plot a course back to earth. Initially the views are spectacular.

Big Beatrice

Pay a visit to Big Beatrice, the world's most powerful cannon. Used in the Middle Ages to repel attackers and destroy whole armies of invaders, Big Beatrice can fire a one ton cannonball twenty miles in five seconds. Gubbenstery Castle is fitted with one hundred cannons but Big Beatrice is by far the most powerful and certainly the most feared. You will be loaded into Big Beatrice feet first while wearing a special protective shirt and tie and matching paper helmet. When our chief marksman lights the fuse you will only have to wait two seconds before being launched parallel to the ground at over 1,000mph headfirst towards the derelict buildings on the outskirts of Gubbenstery. Our chief marksman is very precise and you will land safely on a pile of bricks next to the mattress factory. There is a handily positioned bus stop only three miles from your landing site and you will be back at the castle within three hours using the number 62 bus. A challenging and rewarding experience.

Authentic Castle Memorabilia

Make your way to the central courtyard and take advantage of genuine castle memorabilia such as one quarter scale models of the castle, swords, mallets, daggers, battle axes, bludgeons and fully working flails, all at original prices. Also, why not accept with our compliments, a free of charge, life-long memento of your visit by being branded. Our genuine furnace-heated branding irons will leave you with a beautiful reminder of your trip to Gubbenstery Castle. You will be locked down in authentic mediaeval stocks with your shirt off while the branding iron, with the one foot high letters GC, is made red hot in our authentic gas-fired furnace. Our expert brander will then accurately align the red hot branding iron and push it powerfully into your flesh. Only one minute later the iron will be removed and you will be doused with vinegar and chilli powder to cool the small degree of localised excruciating pain. Our authentic mirrors will reveal to you your fantastic third degree burn-based tattoo and all free of charge. (Women must remove their bra).

Diving and Canoeing

Water sport lovers will be able to take part in diving and/or canoeing while visiting Gubbenstery Castle. Diving platforms have been installed all along the top of the castle walls and keen divers will be able to dive down the half mile distance into the moat. To make the dives more exciting, canoeists will be randomly positioned in the moat and it is up to the diver to avoid hitting them. On entry into the water at around 120mph, the successful divers can attempt to harpoon some of the many crocodiles, sting rays, electric eels, sharks and box jellyfish that inhabit the moat. A beautiful one inch replica of the castle hand-crafted from rubber and concrete will be given to anyone who can harpoon eighteen or more separate moat-dwelling animals. This activity certainly cools you down in the hot weather.

Gubbenstery Castle does not charge an entrance fee and is run solely on a donation system where visitors are asked to offer a donation of no less than £25 and no more than £75,000 per person per visit per hour.

Gubbenstery Castle, 51 Fippery Avenue, East Gubbenstery.

Football Round Up

Gubbenstery and District

By our stick-the-boot-in reporter *Jethro Matabeleland*

Gubbenstery United 11-0 Glord City

This game, played in front of a sell-out crowd of 65,000, was a record-breaking match for several reasons. Firstly, it is the Gubbs biggest ever win against the Glords in 150 meetings. Secondly, it is the first match in the history of professional football where all eleven players in a team have scored. Even the Gubbs keeper Ricky Guntor and their worst player, defender Gary Pontium, got on the score sheet. Centre back for the Glords Ralph Barbarism was sent off after one minute for attempting to poke the referee's eyes out, following a yellow card. This was exhibition stuff.

East Buntyside 1-0 Pollerang

The Bunts halted a run of five straight defeats with a hard fought win against the Polls. The home side thought they had taken the lead in the fifth minute when Greek striker Finbarr O'Shaughnessy had the ball in the net. However, he was adjudged to have used a ball he had hidden up his shirt and booted it into the net when nobody was looking. After his inevitable yellow card he stormed off in a mood and went to the pub. Midfielder Roy Foppity made the decisive breakthrough for the Bunts in the 90th minute when he punched the ball into the net direct from a corner. The referee had been waving to his girlfriend in the crowd and completely missed the handball.

Blurting Town 2-2 Arsene Villa

This highly entertaining game proved to be virtually a one-man show. The Blurts' new German signing Horst Chestnut displayed all his skills and proved to be well worth the £600 transfer fee. Villa were two up at half-time through goals by Spiggle (13) and Spoggle (39) and were comfortably in control of the match. The introduction of Chestnut at half-time proved decisive. This six foot five inch muscular monster of a man from Bavaria took no prisoners. With the ball at his feet he simply ran straight at opponents and trampled over the top of them. He was booked twice for over-aggressive tackling and biting but the referee forgot to send him off. He scored in the 70th and 80th minutes, leaving a trail of hobbling, bloodied men in his wake. When Chestnut confronted the keeper he simply lashed the ball as hard as he could via the keeper's face into the net, knocking the goalie senseless on both occasions. A terrific encounter.

Goriton Kickers 0-0 Skonkage Inmates

This shameful match started badly and got worse. As the players exited the tunnel, one of the Goriton players was slashed with an open razor, resulting in Terry Bubbington of Skonkage receiving a yellow card before he set foot on the pitch. This was a brutal kicking match from start to end. When the teams realised how lenient the referee was, they went berserk. Players were elbowed, punched and kicked and one was set alight in the centre circle. The second half started with the Goriton keeper and the Skonkage centre forward trading punches in the six-yard box. This was obviously planned since they were both wearing boxing gloves. Neither team could score as they appeared to be preoccupied with grievous bodily harm. This unsavoury debacle resulted in the pioneering trial of using a blind referee being suspended.

This Year's Pub of the Year Winner

The Cat and Dog Home Inn

By our tavern and saloon correspondent *Jinty McGill*

The Federation of Licensed Victuallers Associations (FLVA) of Great Britain has announced that the winner of Pub of the Year is *The Cat and Dog Home Inn*, located in the East End of Glasgow. This traditional Scottish boozer is run by Billy and Lee-Anne Residue, who were born and brought up in Glasgow's East End. In his younger days, Billy was a bit of a scoundrel and cheeky chap. He was regularly involved in fights and on one occasion shot a man up the anal passage with a harpoon gun. He was convicted of GBH and given six months in Scotland's notorious Whoopsadaisy Maximum Security Prison. It was while he was incarcerated that he met Lee-Anne, who was attached to the prison as Professor of Aggravated Assault. Billy served one week of his sentence before being released for superb behaviour. On the outside, he immediately married Lee-Anne and they opened the CADHI at 29 Harassment Street the very next day.

Of all the thousands of candidate pubs across the UK, why did the judges choose The Cat and Dog Home Inn? I spoke to one of the three judges, Reginald Vimvium, a professional steam salesman from Denmark. He told me the thing that impressed the judges most about the CADHI was their contemporary minimalist approach. Never before had they seen a pub stripped to the bare bones which reflected a bold statement of modernity. He said that many of the candidate pubs they visit are boring and try too hard to impress. This was definitely not true of the CADHI. In his own words, Mr Vimvium described the CADHI as a large room containing a lot of people, some liquids and little else.

For starters, they only serve a strictly limited selection of drinks. You can get lager, heavy (a dark, pungent Scottish drink), whisky, vodka or fortified wine. Mixers available are lemonade, orange squash or lime cordial and that is it. This pared down selection of beverages really caught the judges' eye as a symbol of uncluttered free-thinking and avant-garde innovation. This fresh approach adopted by Billy and Lee-Anne is also exemplified in their modest menu. Classic dishes available are pie and chips, pie, beans and chips, pie and beans or chips. These are the only four dishes available in the CADHI and all are beautifully hand crafted from pies, frozen chips and tins of beans. Each of the dishes can be accompanied by tomato sauce or brown sauce and salt and vinegar. The stripped out nature of the CADHI means there are no tables, chairs, cutlery or napkins. Food is tenderly prepared in a high-powered microwave oven and served on a blisteringly hot plate. The boiling plate is balanced in one hand and the food is shovelled up using the other hand. A top tip is to eat really quickly to reduce the level of burning and blistering to the hand holding the plate.

The three judges spent a Tuesday afternoon from 2pm until 5pm in the CADHI and were amazed at how busy it was. Drinkers were standing elbow to elbow and it was ten deep at the bar waiting to be served. There was no TV or music of any sort in the CADHI, but, according to the judges, the noise was deafening. People were shouting from one end of the pub to the other in incredibly loud and strident voices, using some sort of quaint local dialect. Laughter was raucous and outbursts of ear-splitting yells and roars were almost continuous. Women shrieked and giggled, with some of them having strangely deep and coarse voices. Traditional foul language was incessant, adding to the character of the establishment.

An unusual aspect of the CADHI was that it also appeared to double up as some sort of very popular indoor market. A colossal number of goods were continuously handed around, with a never ending supply of money changing hands. In the short time the judges were present they saw jewellery, alcohol, items of clothing, different types of weapons and even foodstuffs such as fish and chickens being bought and sold. Another interesting component of the CADHI was the frequent staging of mock arguments and fights. This was obviously arranged to exemplify the camaraderie and togetherness of this long-established typical city centre tavern. Although only make-believe, the fights and disputes did have more than a hint of authenticity to them. Most of the punches and head butts were very realistic and the occasional use of open razors really added to the excitement of it all. Open wounds, broken noses, gouged eyes and split heads were very realistic and it was obvious that great attention to detail had taken place to make these altercations actually look convincing. The trendy, minimalistic approach taken by Billy and Lee-Ann continued to be demonstrated in the toilet facilities. There were no toilet seats, toilet paper, cubicle doors, soap or sinks. The men's toilet had one aluminium trough for peeing into and no toilet pan. The ladies' had one cracked toilet pan within a doorless room. Both facilities had obviously been doused in some sort of up market designer fragrance to mimic the stench of a turn of the century-style foul-smelling toilet.

Another of the observations made by the judges was that every single person in the CADHI chain-smoked. Each cigarette was lit using the previous one, which created a dense fog of smoke in every corner of the pub. The choking, stinking, unhealthy conditions truly recreated a nostalgic atmosphere of yesteryear and conjured up images of smoky, begrimed public houses of the past. Billy and Lee-Anne further enhanced the warm and friendly atmosphere of the minimalist ale house by allowing dogs on the premises. On the day of the judges' visit, they counted about ten dogs sitting at their owners' feet gasping for air. They were regularly fed tasty nibbles such as old pie crusts, cold chips and large bowls of strong lager. The dogs certainly added to the general homeliness and conviviality of the place. It was only on many occasions that some of the dogs would aggressively snarl at each other and periodically bite customers.

The judges unanimously chose the CADHI as Pub of the Year winner because it deconstructed the modern drinking establishment and peeled back almost all of the modern day contrivances that can detract from the basic premise that a visit to the pub should be an enjoyable and uncomplicated experience. Billy and Lee-Anne were amazed that they had been chosen and immediately asked if there was any prize money. When told of the £10,000 first prize, they asked if they could have it in cash there and then. On finding out it would take several weeks for the winner's cheque to be sent out, Billy and Lee-Anne simultaneously blurted something out in their quaint local swearing language and disappeared upstairs.

Underwear Monitoring Equipment

Robust and virile man (not woman) required to act as housekeeper for retired gentleman. Daytime duties will include walking the ostrich, feeding the houseflies and monitoring the biting pressure of my four Rottweilers. Night time duties will be completely different. Write to Sir Gaylord Bloodthirsty, Fruity Mansion, 69 Dismember Road, Glord.

Receptionist required for busy City Centre Mafia Office. Duties will include knowing nothing about anything, forgetting when things happened, not recognising anyone and making the tea. Overtime available at odd hours of the night. Fluency in Italian is essential. Contact Luigi *The Eviscerator* Barzetti at Bertolini's Spaghetti House. Use back door and knock five times.

Experienced Policeman/woman required to join Gubbenstery police force (Highly Vicious Division). Must be very experienced in linoleum, loft conversions and sticking the boot in. This is a demanding role and those afraid of anthrax and nitrogen should not apply. Send your CV to Superintendent Guppy O'Gupson, The Police, 999 Rozzer Street, Gubbenstery.

Getaway Driver wanted for unannounced visit to bank. Must be time-served. Must have short-term lease on vehicle and be free on Aug 4th. Overalls, gloves and facemask of the giant Amazonian river otter will be supplied. Probationary period of six months must be served. Pop into The Bloodball public house any evening and ask for Big Humphrey (Shooter) McGurk.

Human Physiology:
Part 1: The Mind

By our medical man *Dr Rudolph Hatemonger*

The mind is the inner part of the head, adjacent to the brain but quite distinct from it. The brain sits in the centre of the head whereas the mind surrounds it, filling all the extra space with mind cells. The mind was discovered in 1850 by the world famous Professor of Neuteronomy, Hortence Scratiny. The discovery was made quite by chance by Professor Scratiny as she was clipping her toenails and sanding down her big powerful legs. She realised, as she sat on her favourite bench outside Gubbenstery's world famous Anal Lubricant Research Centre, that she had something on her mind. This was a eureka moment for the talented scientist and she quickly deduced that the mind must exist. What she had on her mind was that she had forgotten to buy a new hat for her neighbour's husband's wedding. She quickly realized that the hat would have to wait because she would need to write a scientific paper on the mind and get it published before anyone else. She put her clothes back on, re-lit her pipe and set off for the university library to write her masterwork. After calling in at seven or eight public houses she finally made it to the library. Although she was now roaring drunk, she put pen to paper and set about cementing her place in medical history.

For the next ten years, Professor Scratiny became obsessed with the mind. This led to the break-up of her marriage to the brilliant ballerina Roger Nimble and the removal of her ten children by the authorities due to neglect and malnutrition. However, Hortence carried on regardless and by the summer of 1840 she had finally completed her life's work. It was declared a masterpiece of scientific thinking and child neglect by the scientific community and she was immediately awarded the Honey-Boy Zimba Prize for an outstanding contribution to higher learning. Professor Scratiny never married again but she did have a few affairs with sailors and married men, resulting in the propagation of another ten illegitimate children. Her work on her revolutionary paper took its toll on the promiscuous and unchaste scientist and she first fell into decline and then down some stairs. She died alone in the winter of 1830 at the tender age of 97 while snowboarding in the Andes with her mother. However, she left us with a dazzling milestone in scientific publication even though she never did buy her wedding hat.

The Mind: A Detailed Study
By Professor Hortence Scratiny (Miss)

The brain controls everything in the body from yawning to running and jumping off cliffs. The brain is made up of tiny bits that can't be seen or heard. The mind, on the other hand, is in charge of the brain. Therefore, the brain cannot tell the body to do something without first checking with the mind that it is okay to do so. The mind consists of mind cells which themselves are assembled from microscopic fragments of thick material. In summary, the mind is a bit of the head that isn't the brain.

Gubbenstery Climbing Team to Tackle Everest

By our mountaineering correspondent *Adam Nappy*

It has been announced that the Gubbenstery Climbing Team is to climb Mount Everest. The four man team will be led by experienced potholer Randolph Peaches and will set off three weeks on Wednesday at 2pm. The other three members of the highly experienced team are Dr Arnold Putz, a three-time Olympic gold medal-winning shot putter, Mr Alfred Shambles, a retired gynaecologist and Gregory Balanitis, a former circus lion tamer. Also going along will be Mr Peaches' dog Keith Newton, a 14 year-old giant poodle.

I met Mr Peaches in the foyer of the Tonguemeat Hotel in downtown Gubbenstery and asked him why they had decided to climb Everest. Immediately, he demanded that I address him as Dr Peaches. When I pointed out that he wasn't a doctor of any sort, he became annoyed and threw a cup of Bovril over me. When I asked him why he was behaving like this, he told me to say *"Why are you behaving like this doctor?"* To save time and minimise further Bovril assaults, I decided to call him Dr Peaches. After some deliberation he said climbing Everest was the ultimate challenge for every mountaineer. When I suggested that he was a potholer and not a mountaineer, he lobbed another cup of Bovril over me. I told him to desist from the Bovril routine or there would be consequences. At that point he swung a punch at me which I ducked. He then tried to kick me and I dodged that too. I gave him another warning that I would retaliate if he continued to attack me. He then launched both his fists together and caught me full on the forehead, knocking me to the ground. He was about to trample my face but I grabbed his boot and twisted it sharply clockwise. This caused his shin bone to snap and dislocate from his knee. He let out a massive yowl of pain and I finished him off with a few good head punches and some hefty kicks to his groin. As Dr Peaches lay motionless on the ground I went in search of Dr Arnold Putz.

I met Dr Putz in the hotel bar. He had already started on a large gin and tonic so I joined him. I asked him why a shot putter was involved in a mountaineering expedition and he said it was for his physical strength. When I pointed out to him that he was 81 years old he became slightly irate. I told him I didn't mean to insult him and bought him another large gin and tonic which he eagerly tucked into. I asked him what type of doctor he was and he said he was a doctor of the shot put. When I enquired what type of work that entailed he said he lectured on the shot put and gave practical demonstrations to university students. I told him I didn't understand what that meant and he said I must be a fucking idiot. I asked him what possible use he would be at his age on an expedition to Everest and he said being 81 didn't affect his strength and he challenged me to an arm wrestling contest. He wouldn't take no for an answer so we ordered another two large gins and got into position. Admittedly, he still had a muscular arm and a decent grip so I prepared to give it my best shot. We grabbed hands and the contest began. He immediately applied quite a bit of pressure, even for an 81 year-old man with a double gin and tonic in his other hand. He even had the gall to sip his drink as he cranked up the pressure on my arm. This display of contempt really got my gander up and I put all my strength into a final big push. All of my available energy and power now fired into my arm and I pushed his arm back with great force. As he let out a deafening scream of pain, his arm came apart at the elbow and I was left holding his detached lower arm. There was no blood but there was a large bone sticking out. He dropped his gin and tonic from his other hand and hit the floor writhing in agony. I still had his arm in my hand so I gave it to the barman for safe keeping. I left the bar and headed for the restaurant where I had planned to meet the third member of the team, Alfred Shambles.

When I arrived, he was already sitting at a table. He had a massive plate in front of him which had half a chicken, a T-bone steak, a whole salmon and various baked potatoes, chips and fried bread on it. I couldn't help but notice the complete absence of vegetables. I introduced myself and sat down. He said hello while continuing to devour his colossal lunch. He looked younger than I imagined so I asked him his age and he told me he was 16. I asked him how he could be a gynaecologist at 16 never mind a retired one. He claimed it was to increase publicity for the expedition. I asked him about his mountaineering experience and he said he had been hill walking once but he didn't enjoy it. *"Too cold, too boring, too windy and nothing to do,"* he added. He assumed he'd get paid for climbing Everest so he agreed to go. *"How hard could it be?"* he said. *"Very hard. It's 29,000 feet with sub-zero temperatures and hurricane force winds. You don't look like you could climb out of bed never mind climb Everest,"* I said. Mr Shambles appeared to take offence at my remark and jumped up and confronted me nose to nose.

"Calm down you stupid bastard," I said, but he suddenly head butted me forehead to forehead. It was an almighty clatter and I was momentarily stupefied. However, he seemed to come off worse than me and landed on the floor. I decided to walk away but he grabbed my leg and pulled me to the floor where we started to wrestle. He tried to gouge my eyes out but I managed to snap off both his thumbs and punch him in the throat. He had youthful energy on his side and he wasn't one to quit a fight. He threw a wicked punch that completely flattened my nose and rocked me back on my heels. I knew I had to do something spectacular to finish this bastard off so I ran at him at top speed and drove my head into his guts, knocking

him off his feet. I grabbed the half chicken, T-bone steak and salmon and forced the lot into his mouth, along with two dinner plates, an ashtray and the leg of a chair. I smashed both his kneecaps to dust with a champagne bottle and he was finally done for. I straightened my tie and my nose and went in search of Mr Gregory Balanitis.

I found Mr Balanitis sitting on a chair in the foyer of the hotel. He had an enormous poodle sleeping on his lap with a long stream of drool descending from its mouth onto Balanitis's shoes. I introduced myself and he said *"Howdydoody young man"*. I asked him what his role in the expedition was and he said he was in charge of the lions. When I enquired what lions he was talking about, he said the ones to carry the supplies. He went on to say they had ten lions flown in from Africa especially for the trip and that he would tame them. I suggested maybe horses or mules might be better and safer but he said he knew what he was doing and I should *"shut the fuck up"*. I overlooked his insult and asked what training he had done and he replied with the utterance *"fuck all"*. When I said they had no chance of climbing Everest he jumped up and threw the poodle at me. I ducked and the dog hit the wall, letting out a whimper as it landed on the floor. He then attacked me with a chair and I had to be quick to avoid getting my dome caved in. I picked up a vase and smashed all his teeth out and then pulled his tongue out. He bled profusely from the mouth but that didn't stop him grabbing my ears and smashing his knee into my already broken nose. I was now desperate so I grabbed his genitalia through his trousers and swung him round and round my head then released my grip and he hit the floor out cold. I finished him off by breaking all his fingers with my heel. I noticed the dog was now eating Balanitis's tongue so I decided to dust myself off and take him for a walk. I would now spend the remainder of the afternoon with Keith Newton, the most sensible member of Gubbenstery's Everest-bound mountaineering team.

Personal and Confidential Information

Win! Win! Win!
Win a free long weekend at Mockit Brothers, Gubbenstery's largest soap factory by simply answering the following question:
What is Mockit Brothers No.1 selling soap fragrance?
Is it:
(A) Wet Dog
(B) Lavender
(C) Monkey's Hormones

Write your answer on a mobile phone and send it to Mr Mervyn Mockit, Mockit Brothers Soap Solutions, Massive Donkey Industrial Estate, 22b Ponkobonko Lane, Northwest Gubbenstery.

Woman who only speaks through a police loudhailer seeks another woman who only speaks through a megaphone for intimate conversations about private matters. Phone Melissa Spunshin at half past two.

Retired professional woman in her mid-sixties seeks retired professional snooker player in his mid-seventies and retired professional foghorn salesman in his mid-eighties for a painting and decorating mini-break in Cyprus. Contact Miss Doris Pungiss, 1 Goombian Avenue, Lower East Buntyside.

Book now for guided tours of people's feet. Contact Edna Sybies for full colour catalogue of new season feet. Stinkbocks Cottage, East Glord.

The Diary of Clovis Pumly (aged 35)

The day-to-day goings-on of a dissatisfied woman

29th November

4am

Couldn't sleep again. Got up and woke the cat for a bit of company. He was well annoyed at being thrown out of his basket and immediately peed in my going-out shoes. I grabbed him by the scruff of the neck and gave him a stern talking to. *"Tony Bennett,"* I said, *"There's no point in me being awake and you being asleep. If you pee in my going-out shoes again I'll throw you under a bus."* I think he got the message. He ran off and climbed on top of the wardrobe and started hissing. Had a glass of warm milk and looked out of the window. Nobody about except a moth on the window looking in at me. I wonder if moths get lonely like me.

11am

Woke up behind the TV. Must have fallen asleep and slid off my chair. My lap is soaked in milk and I've got a stiff neck. Had a bath and a cup of tea. Lay in the bath thinking. Why did mum and dad have to go? Will I ever get a boyfriend? Why are my hips so big and my boobs so small? Will I ever have a baby? Tony Bennett started yamming because I hadn't fed him. I gave him a bowl of broken biscuits and he hissed at me. I explained to him that I forgot to get cat food so he'd have to eat the same as me. He jumped onto the couch and glared at me. *"Fuck off then Tony,"* I said, and threw a cushion at him. Don't know where he is now.

5pm

Been to the shops and bought some things for dinner. Instant beef dinner for one for me and a big tin of Megakitty for Tony Bennett. He doesn't really like it but it's the cheapest. He eats it eventually, after ignoring it for a few days. Sometimes it goes off before he eats it and it makes him sick. He usually spews up on my bed for some reason. I don't know why. Maybe it's spite. Are cats spiteful? I think they are. Anyway, he gets a kicking for spewing on my bed and he runs away and hides.

8pm

Been knitting a new jumper and I'm very happy with it. It's black with a big yellow circle on the front to represent the sun. I like the sun. I used to sit in the sun as a toddler until I was burnt, then I'd cry and mum would give me ice cream and rub chicken fat on my burns. Mum taught me to knit. I wish she were here now.

I'll probably wear it to church on Sunday. I like going to church and singing the hymns. I wish I knew what God had in store for me. Watched TV for a bit. I like the soaps and the quizzes, although I never get any questions right. Dad always joked that I was a big, thick, pointless fuckpig of a girl. Oh how I miss him.

11pm

Time to prepare for bed. Emptied Tony Bennett's litter tray on the pavement outside the front door and topped it up with fresh earth from the garden. I don't think he appreciates what I do for him. Went to the toilet and cleaned my teeth. Still got the abscess on my top lip where Tony Bennett bit me after an argument about him chewing my tights. I hope I don't have some cat disease in my mouth. Had a peepee and a jobby and went to bed. Read a few pages of my book and drank my glass of wine. Went for another peepee and jobby and then back to bed and put the light out.

The Great Entertainers
No.1: Arthur Gallpod

By our marital strife reporter *Patsy Yattsy*

One of Gubbenstery's best loved entertainers returned to his home town today to coincide with the release of his new album and to announce his new world tour. Arthur Gallpod, now 95, was in residence at Billy Kludgie's music shop and was signing copies of his new album of easy listening songs. This is Gallpod's second album in a dazzling 85-year career and critics are describing it.

"Some of only his best work," Mavis Belch-Bolch – Musical Pap Monthly

"This is the first time I've heard it," Johnnie Glutiss – Wretched Tunes Weekly

"Ranks right up there with other music," Steve Stenko – Acoustic Arse

"Who said this man had lost it?" Janis Kaboom – Kaboom Magazine

"Me," Timmy St Timson – The Daily Blabber

"Well, you were right, it's rubbish," Janis Kaboom – Kaboom Magazine

"The best album I should've heard," MC Flappety – Dulcet Tones Quarterly

Gallpod began his career as a singer at the age of ten, when he used to entertain the crowds at public hangings. His first hit single, *"Stretch that Bastard's Neck"*, was a crowd favourite and it earned Gallpod his first wage, a meagre £18,000. He was soon in demand to perform at more hangings, funerals and bare knuckle fights. His second hit single, *"My Lover's Kiss Tastes like Piss"*, was much in demand at births and wedding ceremonies and went straight to the top of the charts. He was now at the peak of his powers and was given the keys to Gubbenstery by then mayor The Honourable Mr Punko Dawson. He celebrated this honour by releasing a new love ballad, *"Bludgeon Her Stupid Face"*, which again topped the hit parade. Numerous local tours followed but Gallpod refused to release an album, preferring the occasional hit single. It was apparent that Gallpod was more interested in live performances than making albums.

By now, Arthur was 40 years old and he decided to marry for the fourth time, after meeting the blonde time-served welder Gloria Fantoosh. Gallpod's previous three wives had all died in suspicious circumstances. His first wife, a Swedish embalmer called Astrid Gompot, mysteriously got her head trapped in a vice in Arthur's basement workshop. When police found her six weeks later, she had starved to death. Touchingly, Arthur wrote a song about her called *"The Bitch Has Gone to Heaven"*. Arthur's second wife, a lumberjack from Oregon called Zippo McAleese, inexplicably sawed through her own abdomen with her chainsaw while Arthur sat reading in an adjacent room. Gallpod's touching ballad to his second late wife was called *"Resting Place of the Skanky Boot"*. His third wife was a Chinese hippopotamus trainer called Doris Scum who accidentally set herself on fire while on a picnic with Arthur in Gubbenstery Woods. Arthur's beautiful ballad to his third late wife, *"Burn Baby Burn"*, topped the charts for six months.

Following Arthur's marriage to Gloria, their honeymoon ended abruptly as Gloria decided to visit the local hospital for a random check-up. After she underwent many complex tests, Gloria was diagnosed with a rare condition called two black eyes, a broken nose and several missing teeth. She claimed that she must have contracted this strange ailment while on their honeymoon, camping on the banks of the Zambezi River. Arthur immediately composed the delicate canticle *"You Get What You Deserve"* to help aid his wife's recovery. Arthur then decided to embark on a year-long world tour of Denmark and Paraguay. He played 182 continuous sell-out nights at the Copenhagen Empire and 182 continuous sell-out nights at the Horqueta Lyceum, before being overcome by exhaustion and purulent blistering of the rectum. He returned home to recuperate with Gloria but discovered that she had abandoned the marital home some months earlier. She had fallen in love with her milkman Kevin Thubstance and the pair had moved to Luxembourg to set up their own ointment factory.

Arthur was devastated. He would spend hours sitting at his piano composing lyrics to try to mask his raw emotions since losing Gloria. He released a four-track disc simply called *"Gloria"* containing the heart-rending ballads *"You Can't Hide from Me Slut"*, *"I Know Where You Live"*, *"I'll Meet You in the Dark"* and the truly emotional *"Slaughter in Luxembourg"*. As Arthur began to piece his life back together, he finally gave in to pressure from his record company and at the age of 90 decided to release his first proper album. He spent nearly a year locked away in his mansion just outside Gubbenstery recording new material with his lifelong backing band Excreta. This dedication led to the multi-platinum selling album *"Kick Them Where it Hurts"*. It was a massive success, although some of the songs and lyrics were thought to be a bit odd and were investigated by the police.

The opening track, *"Drink the Blood of Satan"*, was number one in the U.S. charts for over a year and has proved to be a big hit in non-English speaking countries. The longest track on the album, at a full 25 minutes, is an old time county and western-style tale of one man's suffering, following divorce from his childhood sweetheart called "*Jenny Gonna Get Sliced Up*". All 18 songs on the album were released as singles and all went to number one in Bangladesh. It was while Arthur was touring in the Galapagos Islands that he met his fifth wife Doobydoo McKinnon. Doobydoo was born in Glasgow but had moved to the Galapagos Islands at the age of ten to escape her domineering parents. Her parents would throw Doobydoo in front of passing cars and trucks if she hadn't tidied her room or done her homework, so she made sure she got as far away from Glasgow as she could. She initially got a job as a bus driver but when she turned 16 she opened the first brothel in the Galapagos and never looked back. It was in the brothel that she met Arthur. He had popped in for his usual 8pm session but all the girls were busy except Doobydoo. Their eyes met and it was love at first sight.

After a whirlwind courtship lasting three years Doobydoo agreed to be Arthur's fifth wife and they were married at St Pontiff's Orthodox Church of Hasidic Catholicism. For their honeymoon they spent a month in Rothesay and a month in Dar es Salaam before returning to the Galapagos. Doobydoo sold her business and it was turned into a hospital and all the prostitutes became nurses. The happy couple settled down and Arthur wrote some new songs and planned a new world tour. Doobydoo became a housewife but discovered that she also had a talent for song writing. Not long after Arthur released "*Obey Your Master*", Doobydoo released her own version of "*That'll be the Day*".

As Arthur signed copies of his new album in Billy Kludgie's music shop, it was noticeable that he had two black eyes, a broken arm and part of his ear was missing. When his lovely wife Doobydoo entered the shop and sat at his side, Arthur appeared to tremble and his hand shook. It was in Billy Kludgie's that Arthur announced that his new single would be called "*It's Nice to Be Nice*".

The Reginald Pottage World of Adventure

Redesigned! Refurbished! Retarded!

Thrill seekers and the none-too-clever have been flocking in their thousands to the newly revamped World of Adventure, run by the impresario and former dictator of Southern Scotland, Reginald Pottage. It had been closed for two years undergoing upgrading, with new more intense thrill rides being added. It is now hailed as the scariest theme park in the world and only the brave and numb of mind dare tackle its many challenges. After meeting safety guidelines, the newest and most terrifying rides have been doing big business.

Beat the Traction Engine!

A 100-ton 1897 Vimbazian and Co. traction engine is suspended by wool 50 feet in the air. On the ground below, a chalk circle 6 feet in diameter is covered in lard. The individual taking part stands in the circle and looks up at the traction engine. To begin the event, a lone marksman fires a rubber bullet at the stomach of the contestant, thereby signalling that the traction engine has already been dropped. It is up to the winded person to get out of the circle in time or be crushed by the huge machine. So far, there has only been one fatality, a deaf and blind woman from Nigeria, and several snapped limbs. At £5 per go it's very popular.

The Dastardly Drop of Doom!

Twelve people are suspended around the exterior of a half mile high steel tower in their own chilled metal groin harness. A hooter sounds to commence the dastardly drop and each person drops at the speed of gravity, crashing through alternate layers of sheet glass and burning wooden shelves, until they land at the bottom in an old-fashioned aluminium dustbin containing a badger. Gets very busy in summer and winter so advance booking is required.

The Hellish Horserace!

Participants are each suspended by piano wire under the belly of their own racehorse at the top of a gigantic 500-foot high helter-skelter ride. When the super loud gun is fired, the horses are startled and take off running down the helter-skelter at top speed while you are severely buffeted underneath their stomach. At strategic points on the way down, the horse and rider are tasered and covered in soot and flour to add to the fun and mayhem. All the horses come to an abrupt halt at the bottom by falling into a 20-foot deep pit half filled with scalding hot tar. The winner is based on who has the fewest injuries. A must for all equine fans.

The Catapult of Catastrophe!

It's laughs aplenty, for the watching crowd at least, as a huge industrial strength catapult fires the lucky person 500 feet in the air over a scrap metal dealer's yard, where they land with a thud on the harsh, jagged terrain and are immediately set upon by guard dogs. You are issued with a baseball bat to help you fight your way out and into the "Field of Freedom", which contains a rhinoceros and a hippopotamus. Outrunning these two savage beasts is advised if you want to get to the winning line alive and win the stuffed replica spoon. This fun event has the highest mortality rate so book early to avoid adding to your lifespan.

This theme park is included in the recommended book "*100 things to do to ensure that you will die*" by Wilfred Negrillo.

Very Specific Vacancies

Local drug dealer Gummo Lee Dobson requires an Area Sales Manager due to business expansion. Experience of cash collection, street-level product sales and manual dexterity with a baseball bat or chair leg would be an advantage. Apply in person down the precinct any afternoon and ask for the Big GLD.

Bus Drivers now being hired to retrain as Dental Nurses. Due to a shortage of dental nurses and a glut of bus drivers we need over 60,000 bus drivers to retrain immediately. For more information pop along to your local dentist and say *"Mirror, signal, floss."*

Despot required for small West African country. Must have a history of violence, cruelty and general mayhem. Large house supplied, complete with private army. Apply by writing in someone else's blood to Goodness Gracious Wilson, 101 Galimpo Boulevard, Natongville.

Doctors required to work as Bar Staff in busy veterinary clinic. Very little experience of bar work or being a doctor is absolutely necessary. Company car, company motorbike and company hovercraft supplied. Knowledge of and/or lack of knowledge of anything probably an advantage. Phone Vicky Terminology at The Growl and Howl Day Centre, Spandex Retail Park, Goriton.

Witness required for impending pavement trip and fall. If you are willing to witness my fall on the pavement, leaving me unable to work again, then give me a call. Salary is a one-off payment sometime hence. Call Nobby on Glord 100.

Living room floor for sale. Comes complete with handle, control arm, thermostat and dog sat in front of fire. Would suit living room with exactly the same dimensions. Also, complete set of two bricks – enough to construct short, low wall. Phone Brian Manhood on East Buntyside 22.

Alleged Barbarity by Gubbenstery Police

By our bent copper investigator *Cranston Spurious*

Gubbenstery's Independent Police Monitoring Board has been investigating reports of excessive force and barbaric behaviour by Gubbenstery Police. The six-month long investigation studied reports alleging that the police broke rules concerning the treatment of prisoners, the apprehension of criminals and interaction with the general public. Even in the face of overwhelming evidence, Chief Constable, Sir Roscoe Madarse, 59, strenuously denies any breach of the rules. *"My officers have to be allowed to do their fucking duty to safeguard the motherfucking public from the many different types of fuckball that are out there waiting to do them harm. We can't do that by saying please and thank you. We have to get in amongst these fucking shitheads and show them who's boss,"* said Chief Constable Madarse to a group of reporters on the steps of Gubbenstery High Court.

Of the many cases of alleged police brutality reported to the IPMB, several cases have shocked the public. On the 24th of February last year, Gubbenstery police apprehended a petty thief called Jasper Cholera, whom they suspected of burgling a local newsagents. When they got him back to the station, he immediately admitted his guilt. However, it is alleged that the police brought a canon into his cell and fired Mr Cholera out of it directly at the wall, loosening all of his teeth and setting his feet on fire. They then brought a horse into his cell and strapped Mr Cholera to it. They hooked up the horse's testicles to an electric current and fired 240 volts through it for one hour. This caused the horse to become mentally deranged and jump and run around the small cell in an unhinged manner. Mr Cholera was bashed and buffeted, incurring a wide range of severe injuries. Chief Constable Madarse claims this is an exaggeration of actual events and that Mr Cholera tripped and fell over, thereby sustaining minor injuries. When asked how a person allegedly sitting on his own in a cell could loosen all his teeth and have his feet catch fire, Chief Constable Madarse replied, *"These evil bastards must be kept in line and if that means battering the shit out of them from time to time, then that's what we'll do. We take our role of protecting the community from these fucking rogues very seriously"*. When asked why the canon and horse were used, despite the prisoner admitting his guilt, Madarse said *"The sneaky bastard was trying confuse us and buy some time until his lawyer arrived."*

On the 25th of February last year, Gubbenstery police had been on a stakeout for six weeks. They were watching a bank, following a tip-off that the safe was going to be blown by legendary safe blower Len Bownarrow. When Mr Bownarrow finally made his way into the bank, the police made their move and caught him in the act. He put his hands up and admitted he was there to empty the safe. It is alleged that the police put Mr Bownarrow inside the safe along with a container of high explosives and locked the door. They then detonated the explosives and blew the door off. Mr Bownarrow landed in a crumpled heap in the middle of the room with multiple injuries. All his hair had been burnt off and he had lost his chin, forehead and his left hip. He was then arrested for attempted robbery and taken to the station. When Chief Constable Madarse was asked to explain the suspect's injuries, he replied, *"The bastard was trying to steal people's savings so we had to show him the error of his ways. He just happened to trip and fall down the stairs."*

On the 26th of February last year, Gubbenstery police stopped two elderly women in the street and accused them of shoplifting a petrol tank for a Fiat Panda and a set of four bowling balls from the local mini market. When they could not find the stolen property, they planted £6,000,000 worth of heroin in the ladies' handbags and arrested them for being drug smugglers. They were taken to the station and locked up. An hour later it is alleged that the two women had their buttocks blowtorched and their mouths removed using pliers. Apparently they then both pled guilty to stealing the petrol tank and bowling balls. When I put it to Chief Constable Madarse that this was wanton brutality of the highest order against two innocent elderly women, he accused me of exaggerating the whole issue. He then added, *"Just because these two old boots are in their eighties doesn't mean they should be treated differently to fit young bastards that commit crimes every day. The law treats everyone equally and these two antique arseholes will be thumped like everyone else."*

Only one day later, on the 27th of February, Gubbenstery police were at it again. This time Chief Inspector Madarse was directly involved. The police were called out to an alleged breaking and entering at a local house. Madarse decided to go along since there were some junior officers getting their first taste of action. The house was owned by a middle-aged couple, Derek and Deirdre Gloiter, and they answered the front door with a certain amount of surprise. They said they hadn't been burgled and did not make a 999 call. At that point Madarse took over and pushed his way past the bemused couple. He marched into the living room followed by four other officers, taking time to kick the family cat out of an open window. The cat flew out of a small window backwards and landed in a barrel of rainwater. *"What on earth did you do that for?"* enquired Mr Gloiter angrily. *"Shut your fucking mouth dickhead,"* replied Madarse. *"Now, when did this burglary take place?"* he asked. When Mr Gloiter told him again that there had been no crime committed, Madarse accused him of stalling for time. Just then, the Gloiter's pet poodle Jethro Hopkins innocently entered the room. Madarse shouted at the Gloiters to *"Get that fucking brute locked up or I'll burst its head open"*. When Mr Gloiter said that it was a very docile poodle and wouldn't harm a fly, Madarse grabbed the dog by the tongue and swung it violently round his head, before launching it through the TV screen. When Mr Gloiter took a step towards Madarse, he drew his truncheon and cracked it off Mr Gloiter's forehead, which put him on the floor in agony. Mrs Gloiter then moved forward to tend to her husband's wound, but before she could reach him she too was smashed over the head by the Madarse truncheon. The Chief Inspector then proceeded to ransack the house apparently looking for burglars and stolen property. When one of the junior officers suggested that they might have the wrong house, Madarse thumped him over the head with his truncheon. He then yelled out loud, *"Where's the fucking gear Gloiter? Where's the fucking money you pair of robbing bastards?"* His tirade lasted about ten minutes before he instructed one of the officers to arrest the Gloiters for burglary, handling stolen property, keeping dangerous animals and resisting arrest.

When questioned about these events by the investigation board, Madarse claimed that the Gloiters and their dog and cat attacked him so he had to defend himself. He said, *"When scum like that try to assault you, steps have to be taken. I therefore decided to crack their fucking heads open and ask questions later. We didn't recover any stolen property but we sent a message to would-be wrongdoers. Commit crimes on my patch and I'll split your fucking head open."* The monitoring board have still to reveal their decision about Gubbenstery police. Meanwhile, Madarse and his team are investigating a multi-million pound pornography business at Gubbenstery old folks home.

Music Direct to You for Money
Presents
Top Artists Latest Releases

These fantastic new albums are only available by mail order and cannot be bought in any shops. By selling direct to you, we maintain the highest of standards and prices. These artists are at the cutting edge of modern rock and pop and their stature can only be measured. To compare these artists to any ordinary musician could only be described as some sort of comparison.

"My Only Lobectomy" by Hector Pranthious (£1.01) + *complimentary jam spoon!*
This dynamic new album from Seattle's finest balladeer marks a change of direction for Pranthious. No more is he singing about tractors, mice and courgettes. *"That's old hat man,"* he recently told *Musical Pest* magazine. Now he's prattling on about fusion cookery, paracetamol and the rising price of wasps. The first single off the album, *"It's a Plantain not a Banana",* reached number 12 in the Namibian Top 12.

"Burn the Lesbian" by Labia Majora (£1.02) + *complimentary set of blue curtains!*
This all-girl group from LA release their tenth album on the Areola label and again it's a mix of anger- and hatred-based songs. As lead singer Rachel Fallopian puts it, *"It's not all about concerts and selling records man. There's looking annoyed and sleeping around too you know".* The first cut off the new album, *"Teenage Crevice",* is a real toe-tapper.

"Crack Cocaine on Toast" by MC Cobblers (£1.03) + *complimentary handle!*
Following on from his release from prison, MC (or Mr Cabbagehead) Cobblers releases a musical long player, although the word *musical* is incorrectly used. It's mainly him talking about some pretend gang-based rubbish and a head-numbing beat playing behind him. The title, of course, is a subtle reference to his obsession with gay politics in Kazakhstan and what it means for the time being. The first single, *"Don't touch ma muthafuckin' spice rack",* is the first of MC's new kitchen-based gangster rap anthems.

"Dumpety Doo Dah" by Roy Baby (£1.04) + *complimentary buttered bread!* The talented singer songwriter from Penrith releases his first live album, taken from his recent tour of the Cotswolds, recorded at *The Pig and Pimp* public house. His first single off the disc, *"My Pony Kicked My Balls so Hard"*, has been quickly followed up with a second release, *"Death of a Pony"*, reflecting the singer's bad temper and anger with his late equine pet.

"Songs of Piffle" by Darlinda McGovern (99p) + *complimentary children's oven!* McGovern here shows her sheer mastery of lyrics by making them rhyme. Her pent-up angst and difficulty unwrapping sweets is reflected in her debut single, *"Yabadaba Trousers"*, which is still at No.1 in Swaziland. Her greatest gift though is leaving gaps between the words and not interrupting herself, which is clearly evident on the stunning closing track, *"Yabadaba Bra'n'Pants"*. Not to be missed!

Send £55.13 ($55.14) to MDTYFM, 9 Gazza Plaza, Porridge Street, Dallas, Texas, for full address and complimentary phone number.

Amazing Lard-Based Enterprises

Announcement

Due to extreme financial difficulties, indolent staff and the inclement weather, it is with deep regret that we announce the closure of Mr Muppo's famous family department store for good. We are selling off all our stock at rock bottom prices. Some of the items on sale at discount prices will include:

Wheel nuts

Monkey nuts

Penicillin sweets

Born again lentils

Bellybutton cream

Flat screen jumpers

Hardened criminals

High Vis carpet tiles

Backward-facing fish

Undercooked meat

Coded messages

Sliced trousers

Buffalo eggs

This is just a sample of what's on offer at your favourite department store. Pop in this week and bag yourself a bargain. Mr Muppo's owner Mervyn Muppo will be in store tomorrow where he will be demonstrating advanced fish gutting techniques, while lap dancing.

Learn to make your own broth at The Broth Academy. Never again will you need to put up with soup. Broth is the future and the future is broth. Call Herbert Yimpian now on Gubbenstery 1000 to reserve a place next semester.

Have a truly fantastic time by enjoying a Coal Mine Tour. Fully escorted tours take place in the East Poodenda coal mine, just north of Gubbenstery 18 times per day and once every other hour. You will be given your very own cloth cap, oven gloves, breathing apparatus, and fully operational canary, all for the discounted price of £799.01 per person per hour. Phone Myrtle Zoob the third on Gubbenstery 666.

Unusual man would like to meet some heavy gardening equipment and a ripe horse to make all his dreams come true. Phone Eric Turbinate already.

Attack of the Parasitic Mind Wasp

By our sensationalistic reporter *Bernie Skumpis*

The *East Buntyside Gazette* has been made aware of a Government cover up which concerns the health of our nation. An insider at the Government's National Health Department has leaked a document to the *Gazette* about a new airborne threat to our society. Our informant, who shall remain named as 59 year-old Lionel de Bobo, approached the *Gazette* because he felt that the public should be made aware of this terrifying new menace. According to the leaked document, ministers were told of a new type of wasp called the Parasitic Mind Wasp. It has somehow mutated from existing wasps to become a much larger, more horrifying creature. Mr de Bobo also managed to smuggle out details of attacks by this terrifying creature on innocent members of the public and it makes for truly shocking reading.

It appears that this new wasp actively targets humans and is completely unafraid of being swatted by a rolled up newspaper. Whereas the traditional British wasp is about one inch long, these new wasps are one foot long and know no fear. The leaked documents show that many people have already been attacked by the parasitic mind wasp and most are not here to tell the tale. One of the many documented cases involves East Buntyside trainee marmalade salesman Peter Bulbide. According to Mr Bulbide's brother Arthur, his brother was in the garden tasting some new potato- and horse meat-based marmalades when the incident took place. Arthur Bulbide described the incident thus. *"The giant wasp swooped down out of nowhere and landed on Peter's head. It immediately stung him through his skull which made him yell loudly. It then stung him in both eyes and in one testicle, causing Peter to yelp a few more times. The mind wasp then flew off and disappeared. I ran out to the garden where Peter was rolling around in agony. I tried to help him but he smashed both pots of marmalade over my head. The horse meat variety tasted okay but the potato one was rancid. My brother's head then started to swell to about ten times its normal size and he attacked me again. He grabbed my ears and violently bit into my chin, while continuing to yell and scream. He wasn't my brother anymore and I was in fear for my life. I reached for the open razor and loaded gun I always keep in my pocket for emergencies. I managed to slash his face ten times and cut his hands off before firing a single shot into his enormous head. His head burst open with a loud bang and about 100 wasps about one inch long flew out of his brain and took to the skies."*

Another case involving the parasitic mind wasp was that of 79 year-old Grantly Poonapang, a retired bank robber from East Buntyside. According to an eye witness, Mr Poonapang was cycling on the B0001 road between East Buntyside and

West Fampity on a sunny Saturday afternoon. The eye witness was driving her car behind Mr Poonapang when the wasp struck. It flew into him and knocked him off his bike and landed on his buttocks. It then stung him in both buttocks and also on his tongue. Mr Poonapang was in agony, writhing about the grass verge. The witness got out of her car and the wasp took off into the air. She tried to hit it using a catapult she kept in her handbag but the wasp got away. She went to check on Mr Poonapang who was now on his feet and howling loudly. He lunged at the witness and rammed his hand down her throat and pulled her stomach out of her mouth and bit into it. This took the witness by surprise and she retaliated by using her personal Bowie knife to cut through his jumper and slice his nipples off. She then head butted Poonapang, grabbed her stomach out of his mouth and swallowed it back down. The savage struggle continued for another few minutes before the witness managed to fire her catapult at Poonapang, hitting him very close to his rectum. His buttocks exploded and yet again, a swarm of junior mind wasps flew off into the sky.

A third incident took place in Eastern Scrutto. Local resident Yasmin Pumpage was in town shopping for a new corset when she was targeted by the parasitic mind wasp. She was walking along the pavement after exiting Ramrod McPherson's Corset Emporium when suddenly the beast struck. It flew down and fixed itself to her face and stung her in the throat. It was trying to sting her again when Miss Pumpage sneezed and vomited at the same time. This foul double action fired the wasp off her face and onto the pavement. The vomit contained around one hundred smaller mind wasps as well as a mix of the usual fried egg and diced carrots. Miss Pumpage seized her chance and stuck the boot into the dazed mind wasp. She followed that up with a dazzling array of punches, kicks and some savage blows from the ball-peen hammer she kept in her handbag. The mind wasp was helpless against this vicious onslaught and soon lay dead in its black and yellow striped outfit. Miss Pumpage was severely shaken up and had lost a lot of vomit but she was the first human to survive an attack from a parasitic mind wasp. She trampled all the baby mind wasps still trapped in the vomit, before passing out and slumping on the pavement.

One of the more bizarre incidents involving the parasitic mind wasp was when a swarm of about ten adult mind wasps attacked local man Numbnuts McFudd. Mr McFudd was a well-known local maniac and only that day had been released from East Buntyside Maximum Security Sanctuary for Wayward Individuals. As the wasps attacked, McFudd went straight into his well-practised maniac mode and started grabbing, punching, biting and kicking the wasps. According to an eye witness walking his dog, it appeared that McFudd had been stung a few times but seemed unaffected. He soon had all the wasps lying dead in a heap and had started to eat them, before being interrupted by the police. He immediately launched a similar attack on the police, before one of the officers released the Alsatian attack dogs. The dogs grabbed and bit McFudd but he gallantly fought back and managed to pull one dog's head off and pull the other one's guts out by punching it up the anus and pulling hard. Both dogs lay dead next to a pile of dead parasitic mind wasps and a heap of unconscious police officers. According to the witness, McFudd went on his merry way and disappeared, none the worse for his run-in with the parasitic mind wasps, the police and two Alsatians.

It is mentioned in de Bobo's leaked documents that Government officials are trying to track down McFudd to see if he is somehow immune to the sting of the parasitic mind wasp. They would then engage top secret Government scientists to try to develop an antidote made from McFudd's blood. Our own investigations have revealed that it should be relatively easy to acquire samples of McFudd's blood, since it is regularly spilt on the floor during his many fights in *The Demented Pigeon* and *The Silly Apple* public houses. Mr de Bobo claims he has more sensitive information to divulge to our newspaper but only in return for money. Since we have all the information we need, we will not be giving Mr de Bobo any money. Instead, we will be turning him into the police for being a dirty stool pigeon and blabbing important information to a local newspaper. His attempts to embarrass our great British Government will be foiled by a great British newspaper, the resolute *East Buntyside Gazette*.

International Psychic
Nobby Boonalamb

For one night only at the Gubbenstery Pavilion

Come and have the night of your life in the company of world famous psychic and renowned accordion salesman Mr Nobby Boonalamb. This top class extrasensory charlatan will truly amaze you and your easy-to-fleece friends with the simplicity with which he can pull the wool over your eyes and relieve you of your money. Obviously you will be keen to supposedly "contact" some dead relative or pet and won't mind paying for the privilege. Nobby will be able to provide this service for you and much, much more. Nobby values his audience and their participation in his various scams and admits that without the audience there would be nobody in the auditorium.

Be astounded as he gets a long lost recipe for ginger snaps from long dead Aunty Mary! Thrill at the idea of Nobby getting in touch with Uncle Stan, who died in 1973, and finding out he no longer suffers from gout! Be utterly amazed as the great Nobby chats to someone's Aunty Doris and passes on vital information about the whereabouts of the jam spoon! Try to believe your eyes and ears as Nobby retrieves information about buried bones and chewed slippers from someone's pet dog who was crushed by an articulated lorry in 1982! All of these stunning feats of psychic ability and fraudulent behaviour are performed by Nobby while he simultaneously tries to offload some dodgy accordions. This is no ordinary man or mere deceitful con artist performing fabricated and sham presentations to simpleton audiences. Oh no, he's much more than that. He's also capable of making you pay high prices for tickets to these proceedings and is able to convince you to acquire unwanted tuneless musical instruments. Buy your tickets now to experience the best in mystic fraud.

"Nobby contacted my Uncle Reginald and I don't even have an Uncle Reginald!" Jeff Thick.

"Mr Boonalamb is awesome. He made me eat my own hand!" Gladys Moron.

"Thanks to Nobby Boonalamb I now know that my dead husband Ralph has become a woman called Dolores O'Hoolahan in the afterlife!" Mrs Doris Dim.

"I can't get a note out of this fucking accordion!" Larry Chlorine.

"For only fifty quid, Nobby told me my wife is still dead!" PC Barney Cloth-Head.

"Nobby told me I was going to be murdered on the way home and it would be best to give him all my money for safe keeping!" Martha Glunter.

"Nobby's amazing. He guessed my name after only sixty two attempts!" Mr Smith.

"It's all a load of fake fucking shite!" Brenda Loathsome.

The story of

Gotitty's

Gubbenstery's Family Department Store

By our retail reporter *Graham Marsbark*

Gotitty's first opened its doors in 1900 at the corner of Tummy Road and Romper Street in downtown Gubbenstery. It was the brainchild of Barry Gotitty, who dreamed of having his own corner shop. On day one, Gotitty's only sold milk, bread and powdered mice. As the years passed, Barry slowly expanded Gotitty's. He bought the premises next door and employed his brother Fumpo and his sister Humpatina.

Gotitty's was always a store with a difference. Barry was willing to take risks and would endeavour to have as diverse a range of stock as possible. Whatever his customers wanted, he would acquire. In 1905 he took delivery of six leopard cubs, two tarantulas and a baby giraffe from his contact in Zambia and sold the lot in a single afternoon. However, the sale of the animals eventually led to a string of complaints from irate customers. When the leopards got bigger, they ate most of the cats and dogs in the area and one of them ate the arms and legs of its owner. Both tarantulas delivered a multitude of venomous bites to inexperienced handlers. Local baker Quincy Bummety was severely bitten on the ears, nose, lips, tongue and eyelids when he put a tarantula on his head for a laugh. Gubbenstery's best known candlestick maker, Martin Vaginate, was bitten on the scrotum as he sat one evening enjoying a glass of whisky with the tarantula on his lap. His scrotum swelled up to an enormous size and eventually burst open, leaving him unable to walk for six months. The giraffe caused the most trouble. As it grew bigger, it got stuck inside the house of its owner. It eventually kicked its owner's entire family to death before having its head cut off by a local psychopath.

Gotitty's continued to expand by buying up adjacent shops, before they moved into a brand new five-storey building in 1939. Gotitty's was now the flagship retail building in Gubbenstery and people would come from miles around to shop there. Barry Gotitty had seen his small corner shop grow into a vast department store which was testament to his shrewd business skills and his ability to stay one step ahead of the competition. However, in 1940 a tragic event took place and plunged the staff and customers of Gotitty's into deep sadness. At the tender age of 59, Barry Gotitty died. He had been in the children's toy department trying out some of the latest chemistry sets. Unfortunately, Barry inadvertently made a bomb and it went off in his face. It blew him out of a window on the fifth floor and he plunged to his death, landing head first on top of a passing rat. Barry died instantaneously and the rat suffered a fractured skull, two broken ribs and a ripped anus.

The passing of Barry Gotitty created a vacuum at the store and this led to a feud developing between Fumpo and Humpatina as to who would gain overall control of Gotitty's. Humpatina was determined to take control of Gotitty's and had dreamt of being the boss. She had great plans for the shop and wanted to diversify into all manner of different products. She had studied the methods of the great American department stores such as Yooryne Brothers and Quagmire and Co. She admired their style and flair and wanted Gotitty's to become as good as or better than those great stores. However, one evening after the store closed, Humpatina and Fumpo were in the hardware department examining some new deliveries. As Humpatina was examining a new consignment of steam-powered racoon mincers, Fumpo suddenly powered up a top of the range petrol-driven chainsaw and cut Humpatina in two from head to perineum. He took her remains down to the livestock department and fed her to the pigs, never to be seen again. He immediately took the position of Chief Executive and assumed overall control of Gotitty's. He explained Humpatina's disappearance to the board of directors by saying she had bought a ten-bedroom mansion in Borneo. She had decided to retire from retail sales and go millipede hunting in the Borneo metropolitan area with her Israeli half-brother Adolf Berkovich, who was the local expert in the hunting of millipede, horse, sperm whale and maggot. The board believed Fumpo's story and he was now free to run the business as he wanted.

Fumpo's first decision was to open a brothel on the fifth floor. He staffed it with local girls desperate for money and hired his great aunt, Growler Crabtree, as the Madam. Men came from all over to visit the brothel and at one point it was making more money than the rest of the store departments put together. Fumpo used the profits from his brothel to slash the prices in the other departments and people flocked in their droves to purchase the heavily discounted goods. No one seemed to mind that the cheap products were due to the fifth floor knocking shop. No other Gubbenstery store could compete with Gotitty's prices. Even luxury goods were remarkably cheap. A full size dining table and eight leather chairs was £10, a pack of one million high tar cigarettes was £5 and a set of twelve fully grown Alsatian dogs was only £1. Business was booming in all departments and Fumpo was soon one of Gubbenstery's wealthiest citizens. He had houses all over the world, except Borneo, he wore the finest Italian suits and availed himself of the brothel services about ten times a week.

Fumpo had by now acquired quite a selection of ailments. He had rampant gonorrhoea, he drank too much, all of his hair fell out overnight and he had developed bow legs. His worst affliction, however, was frequent hallucinations.

He would see his murdered sister coming after him with a chainsaw and he would hide in his office for hours until his nightly five bottles of whisky took effect. As the years passed, Gotitty's moved with the times and in 1970 they closed the fifth floor brothel. It was replaced by a department for the outdoor enthusiast, selling canoes, bicycles, lawnmowers and power tools. The privilege of opening the fancy new department was to go to Humpatina's daughter, Virginia Galoot. The board of directors thought it would be a good idea to honour the memory of Humpatina, who had never been heard of since her sudden move to Borneo. Virginia was successful in her own right and was Chief Executive of the company that made the world famous Galoot's Mashed Penguin Sauce. On the day of the grand opening of the new department, the board of directors and a selection of local dignitaries were present. However, Fumpo had slept in due to another sleepless night suffering with raging haemorrhoids. Assistant Director of Gotitty's Peter Bloodhorse decided to start proceedings without Fumpo, assuming he would probably be drunk. Virginia was to declare the new outdoor department open by cutting the ceremonial silk ribbon using the very latest Gotitty's Ultra-power chainsaw. She pulled the cord but the chainsaw started with such force that it flew out of Virginia's hands and hurtled down through the central atrium, spinning past all the floors as it plummeted downwards. On the ground floor, the main door opened and 80 year-old Fumpo Gotitty entered his beloved shop, walking stick in one hand and one gallon bottle of whisky in the other. As he looked up through the beautiful atrium, the chainsaw landed right on his gleaming bald head and sliced him in two right down the middle.

Joobis and Jupty Supermarket
Where value costs more!

Special Offers: 10ᵗʰ-11ᵗʰ September every month

Volatile Bastard White Cider
Made from finest rotten apples. Super strong (80% alcohol). Makes idiots go insane. 16p per metric gallon. Only 25 gallons per customer. Can also be used to dissolve rubble, start fires and cleanse a dog's tongue.

Why not pamper yourself with a tin of peas. J&J stock green, garden, split, black-eyed and cauliflower-eared. All our peas are supplied in either milk or treacle and are suitable for Orthodox Jewish catering.

Enjoy life to the full with a genuine full-size J&J ironing board. Comes fully fitted with board made of iron. Optional extras include diamond-studded handrail, on/off switch and loudhailer.

Miscellaneous Meats for Sale
Genuine animal parts
Supplied as powder or paste
Fully flavour enhanced
Ideal for freezing but not eating

All Sale Items now Half Price
Rancid Milk, Burst Cabbage, Stinking Beef, Dilapidated Eggs, Putrid Minced Ox Head and many more. *These offers do not affect your statutory stupidity.*

Save Today
Join our savings scheme and save money every time you visit J&J. Each time you spend £100 in store, you will qualify for a free pram.

Why not visit the new Exotic Fruit Department. We have Ploops, Cunleys, Thibes, Blaborthagiles, Spouds (Brown and green), Moofs and Gomitrays, all at local prices.

Stories of Love and Romance

Edition 1: An Office Affair

By Roberta Monobeast

The tale of Arthur Crandy and Enid Mallow is both uplifting and dreadful. Arthur, who came from a broken home with no chimney, had started work at Plutonium and Sons Solicitors as a structural engineer on the 11th of January 2004, the day after being circumcised for the third time. It was while he was being shown around the filing cabinets and heavy machinery on the dockside by senior partner Des Plutonium that he first saw and immediately fell in love with Enid Mallow. Enid, the company secretary and resident pianist, was a shy yet raucous young woman with a perfect hourglass figure. She had long auburn hair and ginger sideburns and spoke with a slight Japanese accent.

In complete contrast to Enid, Arthur had no hourglass figure, had short brown hair and spoke with a slight Chinese accent, although he was originally from Inverness. Once the two similar yet different colleagues managed to master each other's bizarre accents, they immediately fell in love and decided to share a desk. Arthur sat on one side and calculated complex algorithms and worked out the structural loads and stresses of exorbitant lawyer's fees and Enid sat on the other side typing, doing her nails and playing excerpts from Gershwin, Mozart and Slade.

Eventually Arthur plucked up the courage, by drinking heavily, to ask Enid out on a date but Enid fell off her chair with shock and fractured her lungs. Following a trip to the first-aid room to re-set Enid's lungs, Arthur asked her a second time and Enid said she'd love to go out with him and thought he'd never ask her. The big night finally arrived and the love-struck couple met at an Ethiopian restaurant in town and couldn't take their eyes off each other. Arthur ordered a plate of millet and Enid had a bowl of water and the twosome laughed and joked for hours in the foul smelling, semi-condemned eatery.

Near the end of the evening, Enid excused herself from the table to go to the toilet and Arthur finished off his remaining millet, washing it down with a pint of buttermilk. After what appeared to be five minutes but was actually two hours, Arthur became concerned about Enid and went looking for her. He spent three hours looking for her all over town when he suddenly remembered she was in the toilet in the restaurant so he went back there in a taxi.

When he arrived at the toilet he couldn't believe his eyes. Enid had fallen in love with one of the waiters and had just concluded an impromptu wedding service in the toilet, conducted by local priest Father Gimly O'Limerick, who just happened to be hanging around the ladies' toilet. Arthur was overcome with rage and jealousy and he instantly brandished his 357 Magnum that he carried for protection. He sprayed a hail of bullets throughout the latrine, killing everyone, before paying his bill and exiting the premises. He would now focus all his attentions on the cute accountant and resident saxophonist back at Plutonium and Sons first thing on Monday morning.

Hencock and Cockhen Supermarket

Where lovely stuff comes at a lovely price!

Special Offers

Discontinued Items
Pick what you want.
Ask for a price.
All sizes once available.
Mainly rubbish.
No refunds ever.

Rhubarb Teapots
£2 each.

Biscuits on Offer
Broken or whole, you choose!
Gathered by hand.
Approved by all.
Once eaten, none left.

Heavy objects
£5 each.

Truncheon meat
£20 per pound.

Why not enjoy one of our big tarts from £50. Must pre-book.

Crisps
All flavours:
Rum and coke
Lager and lime
Salmon and trout
Wheat and chaff
Foot and mouth
Boiling Lard

Tosspots
£3 each.

Boiled Sweets
High on sugar
Low on flavour.
Manufactured to standards.
100% Hessian available.
Full price still available.

Collapsible Leather Monkeys
2 for £10
Retractable Seagulls
10 for £2.

Restaurant Reviews

By our gluttonous eatery reviewer *Gilbert St Pranny*

Our gastronomic expert and pompous windbag Gilby St Pranny delivers his verdict on another two restaurants. This week he's in the Lake District where he goes undercover at *Vic Terpid's All You Can Pay for Buffet* and *Devour*, the new eatery owned by top chefs Dick Zem and Pierre Le Divot.

Vic Terpid's All You Can Pay for Buffet

I've known Mr Terpid since we grew up together in the dim and distant. He always told me he'd either become a convicted murderer or open his own restaurant. Well, it looks like he's made good on the latter proposal and his all you can pay for buffet is doing big business. He tells me that people have to turn up or book just to get a table, and the night I was there it certainly was busy, with nearly most of some of the tables occupied. His unique premise is that you only pay for what you order and anything you don't actually order, you don't have to pay for. The imposing building is a former lunatic asylum, surrounded by a tar-filled moat and electric fence. One side of the main restaurant consists of troughs containing a variety of dishes such as horse pizza and dolphin pie, and the other half consists of hundreds of plastic tables and chairs, all complete with overflowing ashtray. The menu is vast, being printed on a piece of cardboard 6-feet by 6-feet, but the number of dishes appears to be limited, with only a choice of six the night I was there. I opted for the chargrilled angel delight with a side order of sandwiches and duck fat. For pudding, I had the chicken and chips. All the dishes were served on a plate complete with knife and fork and optional spoon. It was all washed down with a bottle of 1975 UHT Milk and it certainly filled a gap, although I was quite squeamish later. Yummy, 2 out of 10.

Devour

Dick Zem and Pierre Le Divot have been well known faces in London's West End for nearly sixty decades and have run many of the Capital's finest eating establishments such as Plutty's, The Mouth, Feltch and Eater's Digest, to name but a few. This, however, is their first venture out of London and can only be described as a move out of London. As Zem himself described it, *"It's definitely a move out of London"*. Their new Lake District premises is a former coalmine. A lift journey of only 4 hours takes you 15,000 feet below the surface of the earth and delivers you right to your table, if your table happens to be next to the lift shaft. In the dimly lit mine, you are attended to by waiters on horseback from all over the world. The food is, to say the least, minimalist. I ordered the lettuce with cup of water and it was duly delivered to my table by Paco, an Icelandic hermaphrodite riding a beautiful grey mare. I was pleasantly surprised how full I was after only one piece of lettuce and a small cup of water. It may have been something to do with eating at depth or the fish supper I had in the lift on the way down. I noticed at other tables all the meals were beautifully presented and the various aromas coming from the kitchen somehow managed to rise above the choking stench of horse manure and coal dust. A great night was had by all, 1 out of 19.

Next week Gilbert is back in his native Motherwell where he visits Chef Benny Fuffy's new establishment *Eat My Meat* and his old friend Tashiro Minimoto's new Japanese diner *The Gobble and Swallow*.

The Adventures of Pumper the Dog

By our canine exploits columnist *Lillian Skrondo*

One of the most famous and best loved animals in Gubbenstery has to be Pumper the dog. Pumper, full name Pumper Smith, is a cross between a Bulldog and a Cocker Spaniel called a Bullcock. He is owned by Mr Leonard Kilowatt, a retired dictator from Central Europe who moved to Gubbenstery when Pumper was a one week-old puppy. Over the years, Pumper's adventures and escapades have become the stuff of legend. Pumper is now 20 years old and his very first adventure took place when he was still a puppy. Leonard had nearly finished writing his 1,000-page memoirs and had left it on his desk and gone out for cigarettes and cheese. In his absence, Pumper climbed onto the desk and peed on the memoirs, causing it to swell up into a pulped mass of paper and ink. When Leonard returned he was enraged. It was his only copy and it had taken him 10 years to write. He grabbed Pumper by the throat and smashed a glass ashtray over his head and punched him on the jaw. Bravely, Pumper retaliated by leaping on Leonard and biting his eyes, nose and mouth until he was a bloody mess. Leonard was shocked at the tenacity of his puppy. Eventually, after six months of not talking to each other, the two made friends and all was well again in the Kilowatt household.

Six months later, Pumper was fully grown and had quite strange proportions. He had the head and upper body of a bulldog but his legs were a bit odd. His back legs were one foot long but his front legs were four feet long. This gave him quite an odd appearance. It made him look like he was sitting even when he was walking or running. Another of Pumper's amazing adventures took place one night when Leonard's house was burgled. Two men wearing false moustaches and dressed as women broke in and were in the middle of purloining Leonard's collection of £20 notes that he kept in the freezer for safety. Pumper heard the men and ran into the kitchen to investigate. When he saw what was happening he leapt into action and bit the first man on the back of the head, cracking his skull. He hit the floor in agony. The other intruder pulled a gun and fired at Pumper, but this extra special dog was too quick. He dodged the bullets and bit the second intruder in the groin and started chewing through his skirt. The man crashed to the floor covered in blood. Pumper seized his chance to finish off the two wrongdoers and started jumping on both their heads to make sure they were destroyed. He then peed on both of them. Leonard eventually arrived on the scene and initially couldn't understand the situation. Who were these men with moustaches dressed in miniskirts and high heels stinking of dog piss? When Leonard worked out what had happened he rewarded Pumper by giving him a big bowl of boiling hot visceral organs from a seagull.

Being a clever dog, Pumper didn't need to be taken for a walk by Leonard. Whenever he wanted to go for a walk, he simply sprinted across the living room floor and leapt bravely through the window and landed in the garden. It meant that Leonard had to fork out a fortune for glaziers, but since it saved him having to walk the dog, he didn't mind. It was on one of Pumper's daily walks that another of his amazing adventures took place. As he was passing the Post Office, a nasty-looking thief with a bloodwart on the end of his nose snatched an elderly lady's handbag and made off with it. Pumper noticed this despicable crime and gave chase at his fastest speed. When he caught up with the rogue, Pumper charged the transgressor. He knocked the bad guy off his feet and bit into his lower face and completely removed his lower jaw. The scoundrel screamed in pain as his tongue drooped out the bottom of his mouth onto the pavement. Pumper then bit into the man's chest and started snapping off his ribs one by one and eating them. As a parting shot, Pumper forced one of his front legs down the man's throat and burst his pyloric sphincter and then peed on him. When the police arrived, the old lady explained what had happened and the Chief Constable, Sir Clarence Honeypot, rewarded Pumper with a big bowl of boiling hot visceral organs from a seagull and a ride home in his police car. Leonard was delighted when he heard how brave Pumper had been and gave him another reward of a big bowl of boiling hot visceral organs from a seagull. Pumper wolfed down the delicious treat and then went on his merry way by diving through one of the few unbroken windows in Leonard's house and going for a walk.

As Pumper got older, he became a well-known face around Gubbenstery. Everybody loved Pumper and everybody fed Pumper special treats whenever he appeared. On one of the occasions that Pumper was being given a treat by a friendly neighbour, he sprang into action yet again. Pumper was relaxing in the garden of Miss Beatrice Throbber, one of the neighbourhood spinsters. He was sitting on the grass wagging his tail and enjoying a big bowl of boiling hot visceral organs from a seagull. All of a sudden, smoke started pouring out of Miss Throbber's front door and Pumper immediately sensed something was wrong. He ran into the house and found Miss Throbber lying on the kitchen floor with half the kitchen on fire. She had been boiling up a 5kg tin of the Swedish delicacy surströmming to give to Pumper as a special treat when it exploded and started the fire. The explosion knocked Miss Throbber unconscious and also blew her arms and legs off. Pumper knew he had to act fast to save Beatrice so he quickly peed on her before powerfully biting right into her mouth and grabbing her tongue delicately in his teeth. He then pulled her out of the house to safety. When the fire brigade arrived they praised Pumper's brave action that saved Miss Throbber's life. Pumper sat on the grass eating Beatrice's tongue which had unfortunately come off during Pumper's dynamic rescue.

Over the years, Pumper had many exciting adventures and became more and more famous around Gubbenstery. Children in the local schools were told of his adventures and a degree course in Advanced Canine Anal Itching at Gubbenstery University was established in his name. He made guest appearances at dog food awareness classes and even appeared on TV on one occasion to bark out the news when the regular newsreader was ill, although he did pee on the weathergirl.

Perhaps Pumper's greatest adventure took place in the summer of 1971 when Pumper was in his prime. He was walking along the road one day, about to indulge in a series of pees across a 5-mile radius, when he heard an enormous crash. The local orphanage had subsided into a massive 50-foot deep crater and the children were screaming. Pumper wasted no time and dived into the hole and landed with a small yelp at the bottom on top of a particularly fat child. Before the rescue services even knew what had happened, Pumper started dragging the children out of the hole one by one until he had saved all 20 children. He even went back for the orphanage director, Mr Conurbation, and dragged him out too, before peeing on the lot of them. The only down side to Pumper's rescue was that he tended to drag people by their tongue, nose or ears. Nobody knew why he adopted this method but it was very effective. Most of the children were left deformed with missing tongues, broken noses and odd numbers of ears but they were grateful that Pumper had saved their lives. Their chances of marrying and finding partners in the future were now vastly diminished due to their obvious ugliness, but at least they were alive. Pumper was given the Cecil B. de Pantyhose award for bravery, which now sits on the mantelpiece in Leonard's house, just above where Pumper sits in his basket enjoying every single day of his retirement.

Automobile and Pastry Events

New season's animal gases now available for short-term rental or long-term lease. We stock the main ones including cat gas, dog gas and monkey gas. Contact British Bestial Exudates, 171 – 132 Punkaroo Boulevard, Glord.

Visit Billy Nanabomb's Laughter Restaurant and enjoy the funniest dinner you'll ever have in your entire life this week. We have joke-telling waiters, exploding plates and glasses, high voltage cutlery, chairs fitted with razor wire, a chef with only six convictions for poisoning and much, much more. Give Billy a call on Scrutto 0001.

Does anyone have a copy of the lovely book *"Punishment Beatings for Dogs and Cats and How to Administer Them"* by Joseph Scrumple? Willing to pay upwards of somewhere in the region of close to 2p. Phone Hilda Zard on East Buntyside 8888.

For sale. In-car monkey nut dispenser. Holds up to thirty million monkey nuts and dispenses in multiples of 28,000,000 or 29,000,000. Plugs into rear seat and plays a selection of hymns every time a nut is dispensed. Phone Patsy Gumeroon on Glord 0002.

Treat yourself to a personal copy of the Bible carved onto a bowling ball. Every word of every verse of Old, New and rarely seen Lesbian testament, beautifully hand carved by machine while you wait. Makes a great talking point at church on a Sunday. Available in black or tartan. Free children's high chair with every ball sold. Ring Holy Globes Ltd on Gubbenstery 6789 and ask for Lady Rowena Smenk.

Reasonably priced green yogurt now available. Can be purchased in 2-gallon or 200-ton tubs. Originally banana flavour. Comes with free lid.

"It even works for us brash Americans," Bubba-Lee Zuckermann.

"This gear will recondition any bacon rod," Mr Pandoozian.

"I agree!" Mrs Pandoozian.

"There doesn't seem to be a price," Hamish McHamish.

"Just order it for fuck's sake," Hilda McHamish.

The Diary of Peter Sensipanties (aged 35)

The day-to-day goings-on of a man who hates everything and everybody

10th September

4am

Up for yet another pee. Had the last one ten minutes ago. Don't know what's causing all this peeing. Can't be the beer. I only had ten bottles. And ten whiskies. So it can't be that. I must be drinking too much water or milk. Since I was up I decided to watch a bit of TV. There was something on about a man having a sex change to become a woman. It seems quite common these days for men to become women. Knob off, tits and fanny on, and you're ten grand worse off. I don't understand it. Weird thing is, as a man he was called Hilary and now he's a woman he's called Charlie. What a lot of shite. I'd rather spend the ten grand on drink. Went back to bed.

11am

Woke up because the stupid dog was licking my face. I was soaked in dog saliva which smelled and tasted rancid. I punched Sammy Davis on his cold damp nose and he ran off barking. Just got dressed without a shower. I'll have a shower tomorrow. Them next door are using that noisy fucking lawnmower again. I'll need to throw more stones and broken glass on their lawn tonight. The stupid postman rang the doorbell again because a letter for me was too big to go through the letterbox. I grabbed it out of his hand and told him to fuck off.

2pm

Some fat guy came to the door saying he wanted my vote in the upcoming bi-election. I told him he could have my vote if he would fuck off and not come back. Had a nice lunch of fried cheeses. A pound and a half each of Cheddar, Stilton and Brie, fried in the pan with shredded cream crackers and a pint of double cream. Fantastic. Sammy Davis appeared looking for his lunch but I had no dog food left. He had to make do with a family size packet of cheese and onion crisps. I don't think he liked them. He growled the whole time he was eating them then spewed the lot up on the floor. I tried to hit him on the head with a tin of tomato soup but he ducked and I smashed the glass in the kitchen door. The noise made the dog shit himself then he bolted upstairs. I cleaned up the mess and shouted on Sammy Davis to come down and apologise but he never showed up.

5pm

Watched TV for a while. There was a programme on about a guy who could talk to animals. If he was here I'd tell him to tell Sammy Davis to fuck off. The Jehovah's Witnesses came to the door so I invited them in. When they sat on the couch I told them to listen clearly to what I had to say about the bible. Take your bible and ram it up your arsehole and stop bothering me I said. They left in a hurry. Job done. Two minutes later, the pizza guy came to the door and expected a tip. I grabbed the pizza and told him to fuck off.

10pm

Got on the drink. Beer, whisky and wine. Fantastic. Watched a programme about how to cook a healthy meal for two quid. What a load of shite. Who wants to eat lettuce and peapods? Sammy Davis appeared and jumped onto the couch and sat next to me. I told him the next time he behaves badly I'll bag him up and throw him in the canal. He got the message. Better get drinking. Only four hours until bedtime.

Items Free to a Good Home

Are you thinking of modernising or upgrading your garden? If so, why not visit Ovary and Syndrome Ltd Advanced Gardening Techniques. We can provide the following speciality services: Lawns converted into mud or deadly quicksand, ornate beautifully sculpted hedges burnt down in under ten minutes, lily and frog ponds easily filled in with tar or rubble, decorative flower beds completely covered in gravel, shale or giant boulders, trees up-rooted and burned on site, driveways constructed from the finest sawdust and orchards pilfered. Ovary and Syndrome has been consistently rated as one of the alphabetically-listed gardening services in the phone book over the past nine years. Highly regarded British gardening magazine *The Divot* has used words such as *unbelievable, astonishing, unimaginable* and *breath-taking* to describe our work. We only charge the very finest prices and all our staff are fully available to start work immediately in between trips to the local pub. Visit our website at Unit 501, Intercoarse Industrial Estate, 52 Legman Street, North-Eastern Skonkage or phone Sebastian Chubzy on Skonkage 9991. O & S Ltd is governed by the British Society for the Advancement of Concrete.

Free to a good home. Five year-old mentally disturbed warthog. Can be temperamental and burst into tears and can charge, bite and slash with razor-sharp tusks. Can occasionally be wrathful if pepper is put up its sensitive nose for a laugh. Answers to the name of Jeff Warthog. Phone Dexter Bogrole on Gubbenstery 8484.

70 year-old gerbil for sale. No use in the company of other old gerbils. Prefers to be with aging mice and middle-aged swans and likes to be addressed as Mr Gerbil. Only eats steak and chips. Phone Cheeky Benson on Gubbenstery 6000.

Classically trained child for sale. Speaks Arabic and Swahili, plays the harp and has a PhD in Mother's Day card design. Comes complete with receding hairline, squint eye and bow legs. Will consider long term rental or swap. Phone Shirley Acrid on East Buntyside 5555.

Celebrate the rapidly approaching New Year with a highly refreshing tin of Ear Oil. Comes in strawberry, potato and curry fragrances. Make sure both your earholes are in pristine condition. Order now from Highly Pungent Chemicals Limited, East Pognettoland Estate, Skonkage.

New Album Reviews

By Top Tunes Magazine's *Algernon Buboes*

The Dank Collection by Taylor Dank

Track Listing:

1. *Rotate your head for Jesus*
2. *Steal my tractor, steal my heart*
3. *My horse was not to know (with Clint Sebum)*
4. *I lost my fluid in El Paso*
5. *Stop and think, I'm only fourteen*
6. *Ellwood and his brother fill me up*
7. *My cherry pie is for the Lord*
8. *He's only my dog and he's deaf*
9. *My Uncle Joe opened my locker (with Conrad Hymen)*
10. *My gulch is never dry*
11. *I'll always enjoy the beef*
12. *One man's woman is another woman's man*

At the age of fifty, country and western sensation Taylor Dank has decided to release her first collection of greatest hits, and what a powerhouse album it is. It contains her first five smash hit No.1 singles and what she describes as seven other songs. The opener, *"Rotate your head for Jesus,"* was her first No.1 and it's a real cracker. It is written by Dank's long-time collaborator Cassius (Big C) Bubboth and it refers back to when the teenage Dank got her head stuck in the church railings. Her mother, Ethel Dank Senior, coated Taylor's ears in butter, battered her rear end with a spade and told her to *"rotate her head for Jesus"*. The rest is musical history.

"Steal my tractor, steal my heart", was written by Dank herself as a tribute to her late brother Dexter, who did indeed have his tractor stolen when he was only 25 years old. This sent him spiralling into a deep depression and he committed suicide by putting his mouth over a Fire Department power hose, turning it on full and bursting himself to death. My only criticism of this track is the rather inappropriate heavy disco beat. Track 3, *"My horse was not to know"*, was Dank's first duet when she teamed up with veteran crooner Clint Sebum. The clever lyrics tell a tale of an aging horse being transported to the slaughterhouse but being told it was going for a day out to the seaside to play with the donkeys. It certainly is a tear jerker, especially the stunning line, *"and then Dobbin was sawn in half"*.

"I lost my fluid in El Paso", has become a country and western classic and beautifully paints a picture of a young girl going to the cash and carry in El Paso to buy her first container of brake fluid. However, the tragedy is that she forgot to pick it up at the checkout and went home without it. It's a haunting number and has since become a classic end-of-evening weepie. *"Stop and think, I'm only fourteen",* was Dank's first foray into the fledgling genre of country and western rap. Basically, it is a comic tale of Dank's father, Buster Senior, trying to marry her off to his brother, Dwayne Senior, and her pointing out that she is under age. It's the song that contains the often quoted line, *"Ma papa said go and I said no, so he punched me on ma muthafuckin nose".* Track 6, *"Ellwood and his brother fill me up",* is Dank's reflection on her youth when she travelled to borstal every morning and walked past a garden containing the dysfunctional brothers Ellwood and Peahead Tumbleweed. Ellwood couldn't stop jumping and Peahead used to ride around the garden on the back of a pig barking like a dog. Dank said these poor boys made her cry every morning for over five minutes. Her sweet melodic voice booming out the lyrics accompanied by full-on bagpipes is indeed very touching.

"My cherry pie is for the Lord", reflects Dank's commitment to her deep religious beliefs. As she says in her autobiography (*Danky Wanky Pip Pop,* published by *Quigley & Snarrion*) she was brought up Hindu-Catholic but converted to Hindu-Protestant after witnessing a priest slapping a dog in the mouth for fouling the pavement. Through her catchy lyrics she claims if she ever learned how to bake she'd bake a cherry pie and give the Lord first bite. Exhilarating stuff indeed.

"He's only my dog and he's deaf", was co-written by Dank and her long-time friend and local toilet attendant Billy-Ray Afterbirth. The pair have collaborated before, but never in song writing. In a recent interview in the *Daily Squawker,* Dank said Billy-Ray Afterbirth is the finest songwriter to still be a toilet attendant she's ever met. The tune itself is a statement about which Dank claims to feel very strongly, i.e. why are hearing aids not made available to deaf dogs in the state of Texas.

"My uncle Joe opened my locker", is another duet, this time with Scottish jazz aficionado Conrad Hymen. Hymen, famous for opening up Scottish accordion-based jazz to the rest of the world, really lets rip on this number dedicated to Dank's uncle Joe, who once helped her open her locker at the local tennis club when some bad boys had glued it shut. Dank's gentle almost incoherent warbling combined with Hymen's lung-bursting shouting and heavy Glaswegian accent makes for stirring stuff. The only acoustic track on the album is the quiet, almost apologetic *"My gulch is never dry".* Dank performs with only the New York Philharmonic Orchestra as backing on this stripped down and bare hymn dedicated to Dank's childhood memories of maintaining a moist gulch for the flowers in her garden despite the hot weather.

The penultimate track, *"I'll always enjoy the beef",* is a sordid tale of the restaurant once owned by Dank's uncle, Goober Senior. *The Cow Flesh Inn,* as it was known, was very successful in its heyday and a young Taylor Dank would frequent it while absconding from borstal. However, she soon discovered that every dish she ate made her violently sick except the fried beef. She describes this track as a tribute to the chef, Big Lester Heaves. Very thought provoking.

The closer on the album is the slightly confusing *"One man's woman is another woman's man"*. When asked about this track during a recent radio interview, Dank tried to explain the title by talking about a relationship she once had at borstal when she was sixteen. She claims to have fallen in love with a fellow inmate called Jim-Bob who later had a sex change to become a woman called Prudence Gunzy, who later became a lesbian called Madison McDuff. It's a beautiful song tenderly performed by Dank at her very best. Curiously, it is the only song I've ever reviewed that contains the line *"my love is like a Wankel rotary engine"*.

Chemical Sanitisation Systems

Pavements for Rent

Rent the pavement of your choice and walk on it uninterrupted by pests, drunks, idiots and religious zealots. Stand, sit or roll around on your exclusive sidewalk. Free of dog shit, broken glass and chewing gum. Be the envy of passers-by as they bump into each other while you stroll gracefully in any direction you want. Trespassers get what for. Hourly, weekly and monthly rates on request. Don't delay.

New from Zerpon and Glank, Quality Dog Suspension Systems. Hanging Dog Baskets. Enjoy a welcome home every night as you are greeted at your front door by your favourite doggy in a hanging basket. Suitable for all dog sizes and small horses. Comes complete with cosy blanket, hot and cold running dog food and set of two brandy glasses. Order before next week to qualify for a free framed photograph of a dog licking the side of a boat.

Ron Chutney's Dog Handling Course
Teach your dog to:
Bum the carpet
Growl at the wife
Jump into the canal
Recognise coriander
React badly to a klaxon
Piss the floor when scared
Bravely run off cliff edges
Vomit up too many sweets
Phone Ron on Scrutto 007 747.

Musical Instrument Sale
One inch Cellos
Rubber Trumpets
Wooden Cymbals
Whoopee Cushions
1000-kilowatt Loudhailers
Accordions containing mice
Drum Kits with attached cat
*Billy Mongo's Musical Instrument and
Agricultural Swine Handling Warehouse,
1958 Aging Lesbian Boulevard,
Gubbenstery.*

Film Reviews

By our moving pictures editor *Raymond de Biliousness*

This week we take a look at two contrasting new films. The first is from acclaimed director Sir Herbert Futty and the second is the debut feature from newcomer Bertrand Ganzo.

Sir Herbert Futty's latest arrival *The Pig Men* is a real hair-raising shocker and quite a deviation from his last movie, the historical epic, *The Trousers of the Baboon People*. Whereas *Baboon People* chose to glamourize the daily life of the modern trouser-wearing baboon, *Pig Men* is a nerve-jangling story of the dangers of attaching a man's head onto the body of a massive pig. The main protagonist is Dr Ron Butter, who runs a highly secretive research lab on the outskirts of Ponteland, Northumberland. In an attempt to breed a crack military fighting unit, Butter grafts the heads of paralysed soldiers onto the bodies of giant, well fed pigs. His idea is that when the pig men are in the field of combat they would not need feeding because they could eat any old shit lying around. Also, clothing and other items such as deodorants and personal stereos would not be needed, thereby saving a lot of money. All goes well until the pig men break out of their pigsty and go berserk in Newcastle city centre. On one fateful freezing Saturday night in winter, a platoon of these highly trained porcine fighting units slaughter innocent men and women queuing outside night clubs, whose only crime appears to be that they are wearing only bra and knickers or boxer shorts and sporting dozens of ridiculous tattoos. The bulk of the story centres on the police's attempts to round up the pig men and convert them to truffle hunting rather than mass slaughter of under-clothed, tattooed night clubbers. Futty maintains the gut-wrenching tension throughout and the denouement is spectacular. I loved it (1/10).

The second new feature this week is *Terror in Spunk River Canyon*, by first-time director Bertrand Ganzo. The story is a dramatization of actual events that took place in 1962 when a party of boilermakers and seamstresses from the village of Penisworthy in Devon were holidaying together in Skunkville, Alabama. The self-appointed leader of the group is 59 year-old master seamstress Hubert Babbage, who persuades the rest of the group to sail 150 miles down the Spunk River from Skunkville to Bunionville. Following a brief protest on safety grounds by 59 year-old master boilermaker Judith Vengeful, the group agree to go. They hire a 300-foot wooden raft and stock it with 1,000 litres of water, 500 litres of buttermilk, 100 litres of malt whisky, a jar of Vaseline and 5,000 family size tins of the pungent herring delicacy surströmming. The main thrust of the story then focuses on the mishaps that befall the group on their voyage. At one point, they are attacked by a herd of over 100 aquatic mountain lions and only make good their escape by poisoning the lions with the surströmming. On a particularly rough section of the mighty Spunk, Agnes Lungbate, a time-served arc welder falls overboard and has to swim behind the raft for over 100 miles before being reported missing and pulled aboard. The thrills come thick and fast and Ganzo handles the action expertly. A strange aspect of the film is the director's request that his actors miss out every second word of dialogue. This is very confusing at times and makes the entire cast sound like toddlers. Overall though, a shocking, if slightly odd, inaugural feature from a director with a bright future, if he includes all the dialogue. Stirring stuff indeed (2/10).

New Family Pub Opens
The Buttered Nostril

By our new pub reporter *Olivia Mouthparts*

Central Gubbenstery's newest and biggest family pub opened last month and has already made the headlines for various reasons. The pub is the brainchild of local millionaire Iain Ladypup, who has spent the last two years overseeing construction of the massive facility. The pub certainly is big. It measures four lacrosse pitches in width and two polo pitches in length and is 185 shaftments high. It has over 500 staff and parking at the rear for two million cars. However, recent reports in the press have been less than favourable and that may be due to some of the unusual incidents that have taken place in the pub.

As an opening day attraction, Mr Ladypup arranged for a tiger to be brought in with its expert trainer from Las Vegas. The tiger was supposed to leap from chair to chair and then be rewarded with some strips of meat. Instead, the tiger ate two members of the public who had popped in for a quick drink. A 33 year-old Egyptian woman and a 59 year-old man from Eastern Iraq were devoured by the huge cat as they sipped their opening day beverages. As the tiger was about to pounce on one of the bar staff, it was shot in the anus by local farmer Hogarth Larpide who had luckily brought his blunderbuss along to the new super-pub. The tiger roared with pain and was then quickly clubbed over the head with a hammer by local joiner Gideon Ballnut who had luckily brought his tools along on his outing to the new bar. As the tiger tried to limp back to its cage, local stonemason Roger Dango managed to thump it on the side of the face with two spare half bricks he had in his pocket. As the great beast slumped in its cage, bleeding and in agony, local electrician Peter Nutrient quickly wired it up to the mains via its ears, tongue and genitalia and gave it a few strong jolts of electricity. This caused the cat to thrash about while roaring and vomiting. After about five minutes of electricity coursing through it, the tiger caught fire, but this was quickly extinguished by local drunkard Hubert Spewpan who peed on the suffering animal.

Later that day there was an incident in the children's play area. A large shallow tank of water had been set up and filled with small floating toys containing sweets to entertain the kids. This activity went well at first with the merry sound of children screaming at the top of their voice filling the pub. However, when one of the parents went to collect their child they discovered a scene of carnage. There was blood, flesh and dismembered children strewn across the floor. After a brief investigation by one of the barmaids, it was discovered that the tank had been accidentally filled with piranha fish. These ferocious South American meat-eating fish had chewed, bitten and torn their way through the splashing hands and arms of the kiddies. Some of the more stupid children had fallen into the tank and had been stripped to the bone in seconds by the voracious fish. After a lot of commotion, Mr Ladypup announced free drinks for everyone for the next hour and this calmed everyone down and they returned to their family fun day out.

The announcement of free drinks initiated a stampede of people to the bar and the bar staff were run off their feet. People were gulping down drinks like there was no tomorrow and it didn't take long for arguments and eventually fights to break out. Iain Ladypup and his staff did their best to quell the situation but it was no use. A full-on bar room brawl had erupted and there was no stopping it until it had run its course. People were punched, kicked, head butted and stabbed as the mayhem continued. One man had both arms sliced off with a machete, a woman had her feet sawn off, three women were so drunk they fell into the piranha tank and were eaten and a barmaid was shot through the lips with a bow and arrow. An hour or so later, when the brawl had finished, hundreds of people were covered in blood with injuries ranging from broken fingers to dog bites. At the extreme end of the injury scale, a man was set on fire, a drunken woman poisoned her husband with creosote and two drunken children climbed up the curtains before falling to their death by landing on ornamental bayonets surrounding the fireplace. Once more Mr Ladypup rescued the situation by offering everyone free pies and this seemed to do the trick before the police, ambulance and fire brigade arrived. Somehow, Mr Ladypup kept his licence and the pub stayed open. However, the controversial new pub was soon to be the site of more dramatic incidents.

During a hen night, with over 100 drunken women having a knees-up, the pub's special mascot escaped from his cage. Mr Hee-Haw was a 10 year-old chimpanzee that Iain Ladypup had purchased in the duty free shop at Entebbe airport in Uganda. At first, Mr Hee-Haw was friendly and was climbing and screeching like an idiot the way chimps do. Some of the drunken women started giving Mr Hee-Haw drinks and he was gulping down whisky, vodka and all manner of cocktails. At first it looked like Mr Hee-Haw could handle the booze and was enjoying himself with the collection of inebriated floozies. All of a sudden, Mr Hee-Haw's mood changed and he became aggressive. He bit a woman on the forehead before pulling her T-shirt and bra off and eating them. The other women thought this was hilarious and started howling with laughter. The louder they laughed the more deranged Mr Hee-Haw became. He jumped on top of another woman and pulled her ears off and ate them. Even then, the sozzled women didn't realise the danger they were in from the sloshed monkey. Mr Hee-Haw then went even more berserk when the drink fully kicked in and addled his monkey brain. He leapt from table to table biting and scratching the befuddled females, gulping down drinks as he went. Eventually one of the more primitive-looking women grabbed an empty champagne bottle and smashed Mr Hee-Haw full in the face, knocking out several of his monkey teeth. This stunned the marauding chimpanzee for a few seconds before he regained his composure and bit the primitive-looking woman's nose off. She screamed in agony and almost spilt some of her Guinness and blackcurrant. The other stewed women then attacked Mr Hee-Haw with bottles, high heels, stools and a hunting knife and gave him a right pummelling. The blood-soaked and battered Mr Hee-Haw managed to escape before he was battered to death and returned to his cage to sleep off his binge. Mr Ladypup placated the women with free food and drink and they went back to their hen night celebrations. He punished Mr Hee-Haw by knocking all his teeth out with a hammer and shaving his head. He also fitted a loudspeaker to Mr Hee-Haw's cage which played the sound of a hyena laughing at full volume every ten seconds just to annoy him.

The new pub seemed cursed, as one catastrophe led to another, but on every occasion, it stayed open for business. There have been reports of animals being slaughtered for meat to make pies, black magic sessions using Ouija boards and voodoo dolls and naked dwarf darts tournaments. Police and local authority inspectors have visited *The Buttered Nostril* on various occasions due to complaints from local residents and parents of children who have been devoured at the venue. Pub goers have also complained about being attacked by wild animals, poisoned, assaulted and pickpocketed. However, local police, magistrates and council inspectors have been mollified by Mr Ladypup with a selection of free drink, free holidays and other incentives to look the other way. The controversy hasn't dented the popularity of the pub. Next week, it is hosting the Annual Gubbenstery Lard Eating Championships.

Items of Wonder and Bewilderment

Portable Car Garage

Inflatable rubber car garages for sale. No matter where you go, inflate it and park your car inside. Allow 2 hours inflation time. £100.08 each or two for £50.04. Lifetime guarantee for a month. Phone 090807 and ask for Jeremiah Pobo.

Brick Folding Course

Learn to fold bricks without breaking your wrists. Red bricks a speciality. Breeze blocks extra charge. Impress your friends by tying a knot in a brick. Enrol now at Rubble College, £60.09 per hod.

Dog Hats

Protect your best friend from the elements with a genuine tin dog hat. One size fits one dog. Under jaw strap included. £5 each. Not suitable for cats or tawny owls.

Dross

Discount Dross available from Zerpon Brothers Ltd. Has many uses. Apply to open wounds for quick healing. Bulk up sagging pillows. It has to be Dross. £2 per imperial kilogram.

Kicking Boots and Shoes

All types of steel-tipped footwear for sale. Men's and women's sizes available for full-on brawls or bitch fights. Discounts for gang members and affiliated hangers on. Prices start at £10.02 per kilo.

Does anyone have the book *1000 English Corned Beef Recipes* by Perry Tantoid? Willing to pay up to £10,000 probably. Write to Lord Peter Bloodgland at 42 Skunyon Street, Liverpull.

McAfferty Gang Arrested

By our cross-dressing specialist *Steve Underskirt*

UK Police have announced the arrest of Anthony McAfferty and his four sons. Acting Chief Sergeant Dougie Fusion had a smile on his face when he made the announcement on the steps of East Buntyside Sexually Transmitted Diseases Clinic. *"We've finally nailed the dirty robbing bastards,"* he said to waiting journalists and TV news teams. Police in the UK and abroad have been searching for Anthony McAfferty and his four sons for over ten years without success. The McAffertys have been implicated in many high profile crimes in the past decade but have always remained one step ahead of the police, until now.

According to police reports, the McAfferty gang were apprehended separately in what Officer Fusion is labelling separate apprehensions. Anthony McAfferty, 59, the leader and founder member of the gang was caught in China. Undercover officers had been watching a market stall in the village of Pochungo in the Province of Shandong. Suspicion was first aroused when locals noticed the proprietor of a stall famous for selling delicacies such as scorpion biscuits, minty spiders and club feet in brine suddenly started selling jellied eels, pork scratchings and pickled onion crisps. Police mounted a stakeout across the road from the stall and observed the strange goings-on for five years, before suddenly moving in and arresting the proprietor. When questioned, the proprietor spoke fluent mandarin but with a broad cockney accent. After another two and a half years of interrogation, the suspect finally admitted he was Anthony McAfferty. This came as a shock to the Chinese police as they thought he was a Chinese convict called Zan *"the man"* Wang, who had escaped from prison fifteen years earlier. They had no idea who Anthony McAfferty was so they contacted Interpol and McAfferty was flown back to the UK by hot air balloon three years later.

Banthony McAfferty, 30, was the armourer of the gang and he would supply them with baseball bats, boulders, table legs and half bricks. He knew his trade well and made sure the gang had all the weapons they needed to carry out their dastardly crimes. Banthony McAfferty was caught working in a meat processing plant in Fray Bentos, Uruguay. He had worked there for five years and was head of product development. According to colleagues, he was a good worker and had come up with many innovative ideas including shipping the various meats in tins instead of rolled up newspaper, concentrating on beef instead of otter, rat and walrus, and reducing the weight of each beef dinner tin from one ton to 500g. *"He certainly streamlined the business,"* said Warehouse Manager Pedro de Meedball. However, during a night of heavy drinking with local prostitute Gabriella de Sumting, he let slip who he was and she informed the local police and they immediately arrested him two years later. He drove himself back to Britain in a second-hand Moskvitch 412.

Clanthony McAfferty, 25, was the main driver for the gang and it was his job to procure stolen vehicles and plan their getaways in great detail. He was captured while working as a policeman in New York. He had quickly risen up the ranks after entering as a cadet and only four weeks later he was Commissioner of Police for Manhattan. He had an exemplary record and had made many high profile arrests including bringing down the vicious de Ravioli crime family by running most of them over in a squad car. In fact, all of Clanthony's 4,000 arrests were made by driving into suspects and running them over. He claimed it was a new, more efficient approach to fighting crime. Clanthony was so effective that he had cleared all of the cases for the five boroughs of New York. However, one day when he and a colleague, Lieutenant Diego Hoboken, were updating the police computer, Clanthony's picture appeared on a wanted poster. Diego immediately pulled out his gun to arrest Commissioner McAfferty, who tried to make a run for it. Lieutenant Hoboken had no choice but to blast six shots at point blank range into the back of Clanthony's head and he hit the floor in a pool of blood. Clanthony was released from hospital later that day with minor cuts and bruises and was deported to Britain. He sailed home in a first class cabin aboard the QE2 and was arrested at Southampton dock still clutching his Policeman of the Year award.

Splanthony McAfferty, 20, was the brains of the operation and he was a stickler for detail. It was his role to plan all the McAfferty crimes and to reconnoitre every aspect of the forthcoming job. This is why the McAffertys were never caught. He was meticulous in his preparation and it is rumoured that prior to breaking into a milk processing factory, he worked for a year delivering milk. However, his days on the run were to come to an abrupt end when he was caught in St Dolly-on-the-Dimple Roman Jewish Church in Toronto, Canada. Apparently he had been hiding in the church wine cellar for eight years. He used to hide inside the wine barrels when the priest was about, but he gradually realised that the priest thought he was a ghost. After that, he simply walked around the church whenever he wanted and the priest would run away screaming about devils and poltergeists. Splanthony would pop out to local restaurants for dinner then come back at night. He would have a light supper of communion wafers and several bottles of wine before retiring to bed in the belfry. His downfall came when the priest stumbled upon Splanthony inside the organ with two naked waitresses. The priest, Father Muffy O'Bunkum, assumed the organ to be possessed and called the bishop, who called the police. Splanthony was taken back to the UK on a freight train and handed over to the authorities.

Fanthony McAfferty, 15, was the head chef of the outfit and made sure the whole gang ate well. For most robberies he would prepare a three-course banquet with a choice of wine or coffee to follow. When the gang went on the run, he decided to head for New Zealand and got a job as an earthquake predictor in the village of Rotaruamanua, outside Wellington. In order to hide his true identity, he decided to become a woman called Stacey Titball. He had three months gender reassignment counselling and then started taking female hormones and dressing as a woman. A year later he underwent full feminization surgery and voice training and the transformation was complete. Stacey then got a job grading bananas in the local fruit market and all seemed well. However, since becoming a woman, Stacey had developed a terrible temper and was always getting into fights, mainly with other women. In one such fight, Stacey was battering a local policewoman, in a fight over who had the most alluring breasts, when she forgot her training and started shouting in a man's voice. Bystanders heard her and were shocked. The policewoman radioed for help and Stacey ran away. She was eventually caught hiding in a tree house seven years later and had since married a local farmer called Pat McGubbin. Stacey was ordered back to the UK but she claimed she had nothing to wear. After some emergency shopping, Stacey made her way back to the UK on a steamship and was arrested on the dockside wearing a black mini dress and pink high heels.

The McAffertys' life of crime was over. Campsites, community centres, animal sanctuaries and hairdressers were safe once more. Anthony, Banthony, Clanthony and Splanthony would be heading to Wormwood scrubs while Fanthony would be accommodated at The Norma Pustule Centre for Delinquent Young Ladies.

The Story of Budgerigarfield Thompson

By our bravery correspondent *Sheldon Peepee*

Budgerigarfield Thompson is one of Gubbenstery's greatest sons. He stands above all other men and is regarded as a titan of manhood due to his bravery and sheer ability to overcome the most desperate of situations. This week, a 100-foot bronze and polystyrene statue of Budgerigarfield Thompson will be unveiled in the centre of Gubbenstery Plaza to honour him. To get a sense of the power of the man, I spoke to three people who have experienced first-hand the awesome abilities of Mr Budgerigarfield Thompson.

My name is Roger Satan and I first got to know Budgerigarfield in the 1950s when we did our army training together. We were both in our twenties and were fighting fit young men, but even then there was something different about Budgerigarfield. One day the corporal in charge of our section was picking on me and forcing me to attempt impossible and dangerous tasks. At various times he had me running twenty miles while carrying a piano, fighting a grizzly bear armed only with a small spoon and trying to catch bullets the other men were firing at me. At the end of the day, I was torn to pieces, lacerated and bruised. Because he was my best friend, Budgerigarfield had noticed this and was absolutely livid at the corporal's treatment of me. The next morning at 4am, before even the corporal was awake, Budgerigarfield burst into the corporal's quarters and dragged him out of bed by the penis. He pulled him out to the courtyard and inserted the naked corporal's head into the regimental piano and started denting his skull with the lid. He then threw the corporal over the fence and into the pen of the regimental grizzly bear. The bear wasted no time and immediately attacked the corporal by biting off his penis and one of his buttocks. Before the great beast could do anymore damage, Budgerigarfield leapt over the fence and grabbed the grizzly by the throat. Budgerigarfield's first punch broke the bear's nose and his second knocked the bear clean out. He picked up the sobbing corporal and marched him out to the courtyard. He then pulled out his service revolver and shot both the corporal's ears off and broke both his arms and legs, before inserting his thumb into the corporal's nose and splitting his nostrils open. He then threw the corporal up onto the roof of the officer's quarters and put a brick through their window. By now everyone was out in the courtyard and all hell broke loose. It took fifteen officers to subdue Budgerigarfield by firing a rocket-propelled grenade at him and repeatedly hitting him on the head with a saucepan. Budgerigarfield was sentenced to ten years in the stockade and I never saw my great friend again.

My name is Frank Hymenator and I first met Budgie in 1960. I was the star centre forward for Gubbenstery United and it was the big grudge match against our bitter rivals East Buntyside. Our manager, Bert Fuckpot, announced that he had made a new signing and it turned out to be Budgie. I'd never heard of him before and wondered what other teams he had played for, so I asked him. He said, *"I play for Gubbenstery and that's it"*. He seemed quiet and menacing so I decided to ask no more questions. The match started and I wanted see if Budgie was any use so I passed the ball to him on the halfway line and he immediately shot. The ball whizzed at East Buntyside's goal at lightning speed and smacked against the post, shattering it into firewood. Everyone was stunned. When the post was repaired, we got underway again and the match was pretty even. Our goalkeeper, Walter Rallaboon, threw the ball out to Budgie on our six-yard line and amazingly he shot again. The ball must have travelled 70 or 80 yards before ricocheting off their crossbar onto their goalkeeper's head, knocking him out. After receiving a dose of smelling salts and having boiling water poured onto his genitalia, the keeper awoke and the game was restarted. Just before halftime I was clean through on goal but their big centre half just managed to punch me in the face to thwart my attack. He received a yellow card and that was the end of the first half. During the break, as we ate oranges and drank sherry, Budgie said he would distract their big centre half to let me through on goal. The second half started and it was a tight affair with chances at both ends. Suddenly I found myself bearing down on goal with only their big centre half in my way. Before I could blink, Budgie came steaming past me like a greyhound, dived into the air and issued a grievous head butt to their centre half. I ran through and slotted the ball into the net. Budgie received a severe telling off from the referee, which seemed to anger him. He grabbed the referee by the throat and rammed his fingers into the referee's eyes, which resulted in a yellow card for Budgie. This only made things worse. Budgie pulled a knife out of his sock and scalped the referee, before breaking his nose, ripping one of his kidneys out and finally kicking him in the balls. As the referee was stretchered off, he red-carded Budgie and blew the final whistle. We had won the game. Budgie never played for us, or anybody else again, but what a great player he was.

My name is Gilbert Measles and I met Bud when we both worked on the construction of the McCluttball Tower in Asuncion in Paraguay. The 3,000-foot skyscraper was being built by local billionaire Monty McCluttball, who had made his fortune rearing, slaughtering and boiling down hippopatumuses for the local glue and blubber trade. Bud and I worked right at the top of the growing tower and were 2,000 feet up when the incident happened. One of our labourers, Murdo Chancroid, returned from his lunch break drunk and fell over the side. In an instant Bud stripped naked and made a parachute out of his clothes and jumped over the side after the man. He plummeted behind him and by swimming in the air managed to catch him up and grab him. His makeshift parachute suddenly opened and the two men sailed down to earth. The rudimentary parachute seemed to have done its job and halved their speed from 125mph to about 60mph. A few seconds later, our two work colleagues crashed through the glass roof of a cushion manufacturer and disappeared from our view. Because all of the 500 men working on top of the tower ran to the same side to look over, the entire structure became destabilised and the top 100 feet of the tower snapped off with all of us riding it down to the ground. We clung on to whatever we could as this mixture of rubble, steel girders and workmen raced towards the cushion factory. We battered through the roof at a colossal speed and landed on a massive pile of cushions, pillows and bales of hay. I woke up in a sea of twisted metal, boulders and broken bones and was standing up to my waist in lukewarm blood. After only three weeks trapped in the factory, we were all eventually rescued by the Asuncion branch of the St John's Ambulance Service and taken to the Eduardo de Canter Memorial hospital for a check-up. Luckily, we all survived with a mixture of cuts, bruises and contagious swine pox, apart from Murdo. Poor Murdo actually survived the fall but was immediately set upon by an angry rhinoceros that the cushion factory kept for security purposes. Apparently the rhinoceros started to gore Murdo the second he landed and had killed him before Bud woke up. On seeing the rhinoceros's handiwork, Bud became enraged and attacked the odd-toed ungulate head on, delivering a savage array of kicks, punches and gouges. He completely obliterated the animal and had started to eat part of it before being pulled off by a cushion salesman. When Bud regained his composure he waved us all goodbye and wished us good luck, before disappearing out a side entrance that was still intact.

Budgerigarfield Thompson was not present at the unveiling of the statue in his honour. Rumour has it that he is on remand in a South African prison on charges of GBH, resisting arrest and wilful consumption of a bandicoot and a wildebeest at Johannesburg zoo. This reporter awaits the next adventure of Budgerigarfield Thompson with great relish.

Gubbenstery Theme Pubs Guide

It's always better on the drink!

The Mighty Homosexual Inn

Enjoy all drinks and bar meals with a full 2% price reduction every Sunday morning. Thursday night is theme night. This week, everyone dressed as a babysitter wins a free window cleaning techniques DVD. 68 Clombo Street, Gubbenstery.

The Big Loud Woman

Visit the BLW for a night to remember. Every nineteenth drink is half price on a Monday afternoon. Join in our Sunday theme night and win a major prize. This week everyone dressed as a wheelbarrow will be entered into our prize draw to win a wheelbarrow. 2nd prize is a year's supply of moss and 3rd prize is a packet of fresh water. 70 Fauntleroy Close, Gubbenstery.

The Swine and Lung

Everyone dressed as a hippopotamus this Friday night will receive a free case of sherry and a scythe. The prize for the best costume is a life-size statue of the Pope made from oxygen. 86 North Foolhardy Quadrant, Gubbenstery.

The Bee and Skint Knee

A high-powered nail gun and 11 boxes of bananas will be awarded to every third customer arriving naked smeared in warm butter this Tuesday. 82 South Retardation Street, Gubbenstery.

The Ample Nun

Join in this Saturday's big party night by dressing up as a tin of English corned beef. The best outfit wins a year's supply of pork luncheon meat. 84 Slaughterhouse Gardens, Gubbenstery.

The Balloon Head Tavern

Everyone's welcome at the BHT for a night of fun and high jinks. Have a go at our Punch-a-Worm competition or our Gravy Drinking Challenge. Take part in our theme night. This Tuesday anyone dressed as a gay rabbi wins a fortnight's supply of turkey giblets (sorry, no real gay rabbis allowed). 72 Sponker Street, Gubbenstery.

The Stinking Baby

Now open again following last week's cholera and rabies outbreak. 2 Dregs Street, Glord.

The Lifestyles of Interesting People
No.1: Gary Basteroid

By our easily confused reporter *Clarence Ninty*

One of Britain's most interesting characters has to be Gary Basteroid. In his early life he excelled at everything and set a standard of personal achievement that few of us could ever attain. Gary began his life as a baby in 1900 and became a toddler a few years later. He was born to proud parents Loretta and Archduke Basteroid in Gubbenstery Maternity Unit at 6am on Friday the 10th of September.

By the age of five, Gary could already read and write, cook, drive a car and ride his dog Bonzo around the garden. At school he was a model student and came top of the class in every subject. However, when he turned 16 Gary started to develop a change of character. No longer was he the placid schoolboy studying hard and riding Bonzo around the garden. He had become withdrawn, started to swear a lot and spent increasingly longer periods of time playing with his chemistry set in his bedroom. The first time his parents noticed something wasn't quite right was when they were sitting in the garden on a summer's day. Gary came home from school and immediately hopped aboard Bonzo, who was now 20 years old and struggling to carry the large schoolboy. Gary clicked his heels hard either side of the dog's testicles and Bonzo bolted at speed to escape the hellish pain, straight at the living room window. Both dog and schoolboy crashed through the large window and landed on the living room floor in a lake of blood. Gary had a few cuts and had been partially scalped. Bonzo was not so lucky. He had been sliced in half.

Gary's father came running over to see if he could help his lacerated son or mutilated dog but was horrified at the sight that greeted him. Gary was sitting in a large pool of blood gorging himself on his former pet. He was holding up the front half of Bonzo by the legs and biting into his stomach and intestines. Mr Basteroid shouted at Gary to stop but he ignored him and continued with his abhorrent canine feast. Basteroid senior picked up a loose fence post and cracked it over Gary's skull, momentarily knocking the boy senseless. When Gary recovered from the heavy bash to his head he tried to punch his father but his dad was too quick for him and he landed another savage blow with the fence post. This time it smashed into Gary's face, knocking out several teeth and breaking his nose. This gave Mr Basteroid time to give his son a few more hits around the head and neck area and a few more vicious thuds to his groin. This silenced Gary and his father was able to attend to Bonzo. The unfortunate family pet was still showing signs of life by whimpering quietly so Mr Basteroid picked up all the bits of the dog and put them in a polythene bag. He gave the fencepost to his wife with instructions to thump his son if he wakes up. He then sped off in his Ford Corsair to the nearest vet, to put poor Bonzo out of his misery.

A few hours later Mr Basteroid returned home carrying a large box. His wife told him she had beaten Gary a few more times, mainly in the groin, to prevent him licking up the dog blood. Surprisingly, Mr Basteroid then lifted Bonzo out of the box and he was wagging his tail. However, there was something not quite right about the recuperating dog. The two halves of Bonzo had been stitched back together but the back half was the wrong way up. Bonzo's front legs were on the ground as expected but his rear legs were pointing up in the air. Mr Basteroid explained that the vet had to act quickly to save the dog's life and this was the best he could do.

Several weeks later Gary woke up in his bed with his mother and father at his bedside. He immediately complained of an aching groin, splitting headache, missing teeth and a throbbing nose. He couldn't remember a thing. Gary's parents had decided to tell him he had tripped and fallen in the bathroom and smashed his face on the pan. He then asked why his groin area ached so badly and was black and blue. They told him that was a side effect of the medicine he was on. At that point Bonzo came darting into the room on his two front legs and jumped up onto Gary's bed. Gary was shocked at Bonzo's strange new configuration and asked what had happened to his beloved pet. Mrs Basteroid told her son that Bonzo was suffering from Bilious Vomiting Syndrome and the medication had affected his legs. Incredibly, Gary believed this claptrap and was glad to see Bonzo again.

Over the next few months Gary and Bonzo recovered from their ordeal and they could once more be seen riding around the garden together, albeit with a lot more effort required from Bonzo. As the years passed, Gary spent most of his time in his bedroom, which he had now turned into a laboratory. He had decided to expand his chemistry set and dedicate his life to working on cures for all existing dog illnesses. He used Bonzo as a guinea pig in his experiments and soon became an expert in the treatment of canine disorders. He became well known for his ability to cure dogs of even the most life-threatening ailments and people came from all over the world to have their dogs treated by Gary.

Many of Gary's discoveries are now standard cures for canine complaints and are prescribed by vets around the globe. Initially, many of his discoveries were condemned by vets as being too odd and too brutal for the dog to endure but are now accepted as standard treatments. He completely eradicated Canine Distemper by sealing the dog's nose closed with industrial sealant and removing the dog's brain. He easily cured Kennel Cough by painting the dog's larynx with creosote and amputating its tongue. Ringworm was cured by bathing the dog twice a day in a mixture of sulphuric acid and boiling tar. Canine age-related deafness was easily remedied by drilling a two-inch wide hole through the dog's head and replacing its ears with ears from a dead elephant. Many long-standing diseases that were considered incurable were easily treated by Gary. Curly tail syndrome was sorted by attaching a 10kg anvil to the dog's tail for a year, followed by another year's intensive therapy using hair straighteners. Wobbler disease, a severe condition of the cervical vertebrae, was treated by clamping the dog in a high pressure vice for two hours every day and reinforcing its legs by encasing them in cement. Perhaps Gary's finest hour was when he discovered a cure for Pumgo's Advanced Canine Drooling Disorder. This severe ailment causes dogs to drool excessively with some dogs drooling out more than one hundred gallons of drool per day. Another symptom of PACDD is that dogs lie on their back and shake their legs in the air while barking for periods of up to eight hours per day. This could have a destructive effect on the owner and on the owner's carpet. Gary's remedy for this terrible ailment was to put the dog on a lifetime course of cream crackers to absorb the drool and to suspend the dog from the ceiling on an elasticated rope to prevent it lying on its back. This and all the other cures developed by Gary made him a household name in the canine world.

Gary continued to experiment in his lab with Bonzo by his side until he died at the age of 91 in 1991. Amazingly, Bonzo is still alive and has since married a poodle called Iris Dobkins. They still live in the same house which they share with Gary's parents, who are also still alive and currently trying for their second child.

New From Spozian and Thrattle Robust Remedies Ltd
Digestion Pills

Spozian and Thrattle Robust Remedies are proud to announce the availability for the first time of their new super strength Digestion Pills. Previously only made available to vets and psychiatric patients, these powerhouse lozenges are the answer to all your digestive needs. If you have trouble digesting your food after a heavy meal, these babies will eradicate all your fears. One pill before, one during and one after your meal will ensure you can eat whatever you like and your dinner will be digested in seconds. No amount of grub will be too big for you and multiple portions will be easy. Imagine being able to go to the all-you-can-eat buffet and eating everything in the room. Imagine never being too full for another plate of trifle and the joys of no more gastric distress, indigestion or canine scabies.

Spozian and Thrattle's Digestion Pills will enable you to consume lard by the pound, dripping by the quart, mutton tallow by the basketful and any number of rancid dinners round at your Gran's without spewing. These strong digestion pills are easy to swallow and can easily be knocked back in conjunction with a tin of super lager or a vat of cheap tonic wine. No more lying awake at night with a fat gut due to overeating. No more hesitancy when the sweet trolley arrives. You can eat the lot with a little help from Spozian and Thrattle. Don't delay because these tablets are selling fast and supplies are limited to the billions we have in stock.

Research has shown that people who regularly take our digestion pills are able to eat a lot more and thereby acquire more nutriments and stuff from their daily intake of things. This healthier way of life is reflected in the modest if spectacular weight gains seen in nearly most of our customers. Do yourself a favour and order a consignment of these formidably potent metabolic boosters today before the price goes through the roof. Available to buy in packs of 50,000, 50,001 or 9. Alternatively, you can rent our digestion pills for a limited time at a fraction of the discount normally available. Don't miss out like a docile idiot. Buy them now and eat like a ravenous horse.

"These pills are great, I can eat like fuck," Roland Lipid.

"I am now a massive bloater," Ken Obeece.

"I eat out twice a night and it's not enough," Mr Willard Laroobian.

"I'm constantly camped in the toilet," Miss Euphemia Glandor.

"My clothes are too small for me now," Big Vera Skrutiss.

"I bought 50,000 of these bastard pills and I'm still hungry," Virgil Bup.

"My buttocks are now 7 feet wide," Gertrude Rabies.

"I can now eat sheets of glass and tin as well," Silly Billy Nelson.

"I'm now hungrier than a Bombay Shitehawk," Hector Maladroit.

"I am far too immense to get in my house," Massive Minnie Guzzle.

"What time is it?" Ian Dazed Senior.

"These beauties will clean you right out," Dotty McGillicuddy.

"The minute I stop eating I'm starving – what's going on?" Ivy Naydor.

"What was the question again?" Ian Dazed Senior.

Bargains for All

All types of rabbits for sale or hire. We have clockwork rabbits, cloth rabbits, gullible rabbits, cowardly rabbits, brutal rabbits and a six-foot talking hare. Phone Leroy Pluthian on Gubbenstery 6666.

Buy or rent your very own attractive gravel pit by phoning Gravel Pit World on Gubbenstery 4321. We can deliver any size of pit to your living room within the year. From tiny micro-aggregates of shale and dust to lorry loads of enormous 1000-ton boulders. It's easy. Just give us a call and leave your front door open. We'll do the rest.

Whole elephants in olive oil. Free purple fork-lift truck and set of 12 snooker tables with every fourth jar. Phone Commander Jeff Gaseous on East Buntyside 3333 next week some time.

Lucinda and Humphrey Gabardine-Smyth are proud to announce the graduation of their first child. Mortimer Gabardine-Smyth (the third) has graduated from The Opulent School for Dullards with a conditional third class degree in Advanced Sod All.

Gubbenstery Gun Oil Society is delighted to announce the marriage of their chairwoman Miss Beatrice Gunblast to unknown local man Mr Billy Stinkybobo. The service will take place four years from now at half one in the afternoon at Our Lady of the Titsanass Holy Bijesus Church.

Ultra-high temperature curtains with complimentary frog for sale. 60p or nearest offer. No time wasters. Phone Keith Diddums on East Buntyside 1111.

"I don't drink alcohol anymore – I just drink Blooteraid," Larry Buntage.

"It's so strong I forgot I had a hangover," Sir Robert Henpole.

"I think they should sell it in bigger sizes," Ron Botswana.

"I can drink 20 pints of Scrumpy at night and Blooteraid sorts me out," Ryan Stagdoo.

"If I drink Blooteraid at night I need 20 pints of Scrumpy in the morning," Ryan Stagdoo.

"I accidentally spilled some on my stepchild and her head came off," Mabel Zalron (Mr).

"I love the flavour – it's so creamy," Leonard Arscheex.

"Blooteraid can also be used to remove chewing gum from a moth's eye," Dr Arthur Giblets.

"Don't buy it, it's awful – it tastes like my Grandfather's phlegm," Brian Penitensharry.

"I love it – two half-pint shandies every night and no hangover," Miss Muriel Dronk.

Gubbenstery News in Brief

Compiled by our muckraker *Jumbo Bunhead*

A man is in hospital after having his tongue bitten off by local horse Dobbin Simpson. Horace Hyppolyte was feeding the horse at the time of the incident. He told our reporter (using sign language) that he was in the process of feeding the horse a mixture of mentholyptus, chilli, mustard and wasabi paste when the bad tempered stallion launched the unprovoked attack. Mr Hippolyte's replacement plasticine tongue is still on back order.

In a separate incident, a woman is in hospital after being run over by a cat. Camilla Podium was walking down her garden path when the passing cat severely brushed against her leg. Before Miss Podium could smash the cat's head open with a brick, it escaped through a hedge. Police are advising local residents to carry an axe at all times.

It has been revealed that consumption of English corned beef in Gubbenstery has more than doubled over the last week. ECB spokesman Dennis Paradiddle says this is great news.

Local man Gary Hithere is suing another local man, Big Arthur Potent, for damages after it was alleged that he backed into him. Hithere claims he was standing on the pavement when he saw Potent walking backwards towards him. Hithere said that before he could get out of the way *"I had a mouthful of arse"*. Family have been notified.

Notorious Gubbenstery criminal Tother Gobson has escaped yet again from Gubbenstery maximum security prison. It's the nineteenth time Gobson has escaped, but being relatively stupid, he is usually caught within the hour. The last time he escaped he said that he only left the prison grounds temporarily to retrieve his talking parrot Quackers Nelson.

The proposed new skyscraper, The Gubbenstery Megatower, has been given the go ahead. The new 10-mile high building constructed entirely from clay will be Gubbenstery's second tallest building after The Gubbenstery Obelisk at 10 miles and one foot high. Local mum of ten, Kelly-Marie Repellent, says she knows nothing about either building.

Gubbenstery Lord Mayor Pulchritude McKenzie has unexpectedly resigned. The 59 year-old was under investigation by police for allegedly tying a bowling ball to a dog's tail. The 5 year-old Yorkshire terrier called David Boyce was so scared it ran for 22 miles to escape the terrifying bowling ball following just three feet behind it. David eventually collapsed in a pool of dog blood when his legs were worn down to bloody stumps.

The Head of Gubbenstery Police, Superintendent Roland Clitoris, was yesterday convicted of drink driving while committing GBH. He was caught doing 156mph in a 30mph zone outside a school while battering his wife, who was in the passenger seat. Superintendent Clitoris regrets the whole incident and on reflection says he should have battered his wife before he left the house.

A major scientific breakthrough was announced yesterday at Gubbenstery College. Professor Humphrey Bongo, a janitor at the college, couldn't hold back his excitement when he said his team had made an astonishing discovery, although they weren't quite sure what it was. *"We noticed something in the lab and decided to closely monitor it. Further tests are being carried out to identify what the fuck it might be,"* said the delighted Professor.

The Baboon Hazard

By our baboon safety correspondent *Roger Gapeworm*

It has recently come to the attention of Gubbenstery Police that a very large troop of baboons has set up residence at the western edge of Gubbenstery just behind the Yodelling College. Chief Sergeant Ray Panty of Gubbenstery's specialist Monkey Division says that it is still unclear where the baboons came from, although he suspects they hitched a lift on a steamship from Africa. Although CS Panty's expertise is mainly in handling mandrills, proboscis monkeys and giraffes, he is also skilled at dealing with baboons, having recently graduated from Gubbenstery's Baboon College with a third class degree in worm motivational techniques and hay baling. According to CS Panty, the troop consists of about 150,000 baboons spread over an area of two square miles, and this is putting a lot of pressure on the baboon's normal food sources, which comprises antelopes, other monkeys and low fat yoghurt. The lack of antelopes, other monkeys and low fat yoghurt in downtown Gubbenstery means that the baboons have had to adapt to local conditions and forage for their dinner.

Police have received reports of baboon activity from local residents and there is growing concern that the baboons may actually be highly dangerous predators, rather than playful, idiotic monkeys. Local unemployed man Clarence Whooping told me of a terrifying experience he had with the baboons. He was sitting at home having a quiet drink at eight in the morning when a large baboon came crashing through his window and landed on his lap. It immediately bit him on the cheek, removing a large swath of flesh causing Mr Whooping's tongue to loll out the side of his face. It then bit through his new jumper into his stomach and proceeded to feed upon Mr Whooping's innards. Only quick thinking by Mr Whooping saved his life and most of his innards. In the nick of time he bashed the animal's head with an empty 5-litre whisky bottle and split its skull open. He then quickly jammed a large ornamental brass penis into the baboon's skull, dislodging part of its brain onto the carpet. The brass penis was a gift given to Mr Whooping by his son who had brought it back from the duty free shop at Entebbe airport in Uganda. The penis insertion killed the rampaging baboon and it slumped to the floor. However, Mr Whooping was so terrified of further baboon attacks that he sat in his chair all day drinking whisky, armed only with the brass penis, until his wife came home at 5pm to make his dinner.

Another victim of the hellish baboon attacks was the oldest bakery in Gubbenstery. The Beatrice Vile family bakery was established in Gubbenstery in

1995 and is run by 92 year-old Beatrice Vile and her two daughters, Minnie, 72, and Maxie, 22. According to Beatrice, rampaging troops of baboons burst their way into the shop and steal cakes, pies and anything they can grab. Once they get what they came for, they would race out of the door and run down the street screeching. She says her customers are terrified, although occasionally they manage to grab one of the baboons and smash it to pieces with hammers and bricks. Ms Vile says all her customers now come to her shop armed. She says they bring hammers, knives, baseball bats and the occasional firearm. They are determined not to be deprived of the famous Vile cakes and pies. Recently, Minnie and Maxie installed industrial strength netting above the door. Their plan is to ensnare the baboons as they enter the shop and immediately douse them in petrol and set them alight. As Beatrice put it, *"No fucking monkey is going to deprive me of ma muthafuckin' livelihood, no fucking way man"*.

One of the scariest baboon attacks was at Gubbenstery Stadium. Gubbenstery United were playing an important third round cup game against Glord City and were 2-0 up at half-time. As the packed crowd of over 59,001 enjoyed their half-time snacks of jugged hare and arctic roll, the baboons struck. Obviously enticed by the tempting cooking aromas wafting out of the stadium, hundreds of baboons easily climbed over the outer wall of the stadium and immediately began a mass attack on the spectators. Because the stadium was packed, the baboons could easily run across the heads of all the people, using their clever, grasping monkey feet, snatching food as they went. However, things turned nasty when the food ran out. The baboons were now in attack mode and were still hungry. With no snacks left, the baboons started biting chunks out of the terrified fans, mainly concentrating on cheeks, forehead, ears and lips. It turned into a bloodbath as the crazed, big-toothed monkeys went mental. Just as it looked like there was going to be a sea of dead football fans, help suddenly arrived from an unusual source. Earlier on and throughout the first half, violent, booze-fuelled hooligans from Gubbenstery and Glord had been fighting each other with an array of weapons including claw hammers, lead pipes, knives, machine guns and the now appropriate monkey wrenches. The well-drilled louts now focused their attention on the baboons and commenced an all-out brawl of the sort never witnessed in Gubbenstery before. The baboons, which were completely unarmed, fought bravely but were no match for this uneducated but potent fighting force. As innocent fans ran for cover, the louts attacked the baboons with immeasurable ferocity. The baboons were slashed, shot, kicked and battered and the sound of howling and screeching was deafening. Arms were cut off, heads smashed in and the odd baboon was dispatched by flame thrower. The baboons did their best to fight back by biting, scratching and head butting but it was no use. They were out-matched by this mob of barbarian football supporters and the ones that were still alive decided to retreat. About two hundred baboons were killed and one hooligan suffered a stubbed toe. The baboon body parts were quickly cleared away, the hooligans went back to fighting each other and the game restarted. A second half hat-trick by centre forward Albert Cruntage gave Gubbenstery a 5-0 win. They now go on to play Gomage Town in the fourth round.

Because of the sheer number of baboons in the area, police have become overwhelmed and have had to turn to local gang leaders for help. CS Panty has hooked up with Doris Vore, leader of the Gubbenstery Strumpets, an all-girl gang renowned for their violence, bawdy behaviour and inability to reverse into a parking space. Also lined up to lend a hand is notorious gang leader Hank Beastman, leader of the Gubbenstery Slaughtermen, renowned for disembowelling rival gang members and setting fire to religious leaders. CS Panty has been holding secret talks with Vore and Beastman and they have been drawing up plans to tackle the baboons. Panty has had to agree to a complete amnesty for all of Vore and Beastman's gang members, relating to crimes such as drive-by shootings, slashings, bomb making, animal rustling and mass slaughter. He says this will be a small price to pay if it results in complete eradication of the baboons and a return to normal life for the residents of western Gubbenstery. It is rumoured that Panty, Vore and Beastman have already planned an all-out attack on baboon headquarters next Friday night after the pubs shut but this has yet to be confirmed.

Steam-Powered Tights for Hire

Decaying gentleman, the wrong side of 30 (81) seeks happy-go-lucky young lady 20-25 to do housework, gardening, dog walking and light engineering. Must be cheery, daft and usually naked. No need for any intelligence. Fluency in cake baking and further nakedness would be an advantage. Write to Sir Horace Nangpole the Third at Nangpole Towers, Gubbenstery.

Learn to play tricks on domestic cats. Phone Dr Guntis Mackenzie on Glord 0000 and you will be able to attach clothes pegs to a cat's tail, put a sock over a cat's head, bang cymbals together when your cat's sleeping, let your cat play with blown up balloons and replace your cat's milk with fortified wine.

Learn to Hop
Fully unsupervised hopping tuition now available with ex-Olympic hopping champion Tina Bawsac. Tina is licenced to teach all hopping levels from beginner (can hardly stand on two feet) right up to advanced (restless halfwit). Trust Tina to make you the hopper you've always wanted to be. Phone Gubbenstery 0001 and say the special hopping code word "hoppetyboppety".

Treetops in brine now available. Enjoy this year's succulent young treetops in quality Irish brine. Sold by the pound, kilogram and hectare. £100 per 1g jar. For only £100 extra we will put the lid of the jar on slightly less tight. Call Peter Konboil at Nidorous Elevated Tree Supplies Ltd.

Goblins Back in Scotland

By our enchanted creature specialist *Spanky MacLean*

After a period of over 100 years, goblins are once again resident in Scotland. Earlier alleged sightings by drunkards and simpletons had been doubted by the authorities, but their presence has been confirmed photographically in the small Scottish village of Glabber on the Kintyre Peninsula by Mrs Doris Glurrance. Mrs Glurrance, a former naval fighter pilot, claims that the goblins come into her back garden to steal fruit, vegetables and clothes from her washing line. She says she has even met the head goblin, a chap called Iain Hobgoblin, and he is quite friendly, although he did climb on top of her and sit on her head at one point. He told her that it wasn't only goblins that had settled in the area. As far as he knew, there were a handful of gremlins, imps, pixies and the odd gargoyle with homes in the area. According to Mrs Glurrance, the wee folk only come out at night and seem to have a great time at the bottom of her garden or in the woods having parties and singsongs.

However, some of the other residents of Glabber have told local police that the goblins and their pals are becoming a nuisance. They say they are giggling and laughing outside bedroom windows at night and placing things where they shouldn't be. Mr Maurice Noxious of the neighbouring village of Pluppington claims that a goblin or perhaps some sort of evil elf put a spell on his dog. The dog, a mongrel called Robert Doolally, is now able to speak and has repeatedly told Mr Noxious to *"Fuck off"* when asked if he wanted to go for walkies. Also, other dogs in the area have been seen jumping over houses, shopping and eating in restaurants. It is also reported that a cat was seen smoking a pipe. These and other strange goings-on are all attributed to the goblins and their associates. When interviewed by local police, the head gremlin, Mrs Betsy O'Gremlin said that she and her fellow wee folk were only doing what came naturally to them. It is their birthright to steal things, cast spells and set fire to people's trousers. A police spokesman, Sergeant Tony Maniac, said the wee folk are welcome to stay as long as they bring his car back and put a spell on his wife to make her stop nagging.

Goblins and elves were once widespread across the whole of Europe and some were even kept as pets by the rich and famous. Lord Peter Nanty of South Oxford once owned a goblin and a gremlin and would let them loose on guests who attended his lavish parties. It is rumoured that guests hated going to his parties because of the behaviour of the wee folk. On one occasion a guest had his tongue pulled off by the gremlin, who then ate it at the dining table. The most famous outrage was at the

Lord's 60th birthday party in 1908. One of the guests, The Duke of Helensburgh, went to the lavatory and was suddenly accosted by the goblin who grabbed the Duke's penis. The goblin held on to the penis for the rest of the evening and could be seen swinging between the Duke's legs whenever he walked around. The goblin had to be shot off the penis by a police marksman using a blunderbuss, which caused a minor flesh wound to the Duke's foreskin. Lord Nanty was subsequently banned from keeping malevolent creatures in the house, although he was permitted to own an imp and a French-speaking ogre.

Any sightings of goblins or other mischievous wee folk should be reported immediately by sending a letter to Lieutenant Corporal Archibald Bartholinsgland, 2nd Battalion of Fighting Gibbons, Orangutan Barracks, Ape Street, East Buntyside.

Classified Starters and Main Courses

Visit the beautiful mountains of Chicago. Take the cable car to the top of Mount Funboy. At 98,000 feet, this is the tallest mountain in the Chicago area. Call in to the zoo and help the staff feed the caterpillars and wasps. For more information on what may or may not be the holiday of a lifetime, Email Jim-Bob Razzmatazz any Tuesday before the cartoons start at jbr.bumpkin@simpleton.com.

Today is National Liver and Onions Day so why not celebrate by enjoying a right bellyful of liver and onions, washed down with a refreshing pint of Milk of Magnesia. For more information about liver or onions call the L & O hotline from your local telephone.

Large brown dog called Roger Taylor seeks human man with own car to drive long distances with my head out of the window. Email: rtaylor@barkshire.woof.

Partially Qualified Doctor can treat left eye, back of neck, right thumb, some hair, bottom of left ankle, most of the tongue, all of the arse, some of the innards, inside of nose and a few other bits and bobs of anatomy. Call Dr Tyrone Boobies, 34 Cutthroat Street, North Gubbenstery.

Selection of cutting remarks now available. Amaze your friends with your new put downs and barbed comments. Phone Geronimo McDougall a bit later on.

Unusual Animal Facts: Vol.1

Compiled by our beast expert *Elmer Hawbaw*

The Hawaiian coughing monkey is the only known non-human creature to voluntarily smoke cigarettes. This has led to their distinctive raking cough which brings a smile to the faces of tourists. They never buy their own cigarettes, relying mainly on thieving them from passers-by and breaking into duty free shops.

The world's last surviving talking dog died in Cape Town in 1911. Ian Thompson was a German shepherd and made a living commentating on horse races. He was bilingual and could commentate in English and Afrikaans, although strangely not German. In later years he took to swearing and hurling abuse at people if they didn't take him walkies or offer him dog biscuits. Ian is buried next to his brother, Barry Thompson, on the Isle of Wight ferry.

The luckiest cat ever was a black and white tabby called Pauline Smith. Pauline was travelling with her owner, the actress Gilda de Manding, on a transatlantic flight from Los Angeles to New York when she was accidentally sucked out of a broken window. Pauline fell 35,000 feet and amazingly landed feet first next to a mouse in a field just outside Stumukontentz, Indiana. After eating the mouse Pauline settled into a luxury cattery in Indianapolis and lived to be 39, raising 2,000 kittens and 118,000 grand kittens.

The racehorse with the worst temper in history was the notorious grey mare Resentful Bint. RB, as she was known, was a superb thoroughbred and won many races, but this success came at a price. On most occasions when the jockey would be dismounting in the paddock, he would immediately be kicked to death by RB. The owner, Lord Sulphate of Campbeltown, overlooked these small indiscretions as long as RB kept winning. However, on the 1st of June 1972, RB had just won the Hiphop stakes by a length and a half from Guppo's Belch and was about to kick jockey Paddy O'Dublin to death when she suddenly bolted into the crowd and trampled 16 people to death and wounded 90 others by biting. This proved to be the last outrage conducted by RB and the next morning Lord Sulphate put a hand grenade in her bucket of oats and blew her head clean off. There is a statue of the irritable equine in Ruud van Hire national park in Rotterdam.

The only recorded case of a fully-grown male African lion being a homosexual was that of the 7 year-old specimen Martin Mince. He was easily captured by poachers in 1991 in Tanzania behind a joojoo bush wearing arseless trousers and a captain's hat. He was transferred to Berlin Zoo where he was given his own cage overlooking a lily pond and flowerbed. He spent all his time sitting in a deckchair looking at women's magazines and whistling at other male lions, which had to be kept in a separate enclosure. In an attempt to get him to hunt, staff would put zebra and wildebeest in his cage but Martin always ended up sharing a salad with the zebra and wildebeest.

Despite living in a one-bedroom flat in Drumchapel on the outskirts of Glasgow, Torrance MacLeod, or Tormac as his friends called him, owned a Ugandan silverback mountain gorilla called Gaylord Odongo. Tormac would race Gaylord to see who could finish a bottle of the tonic wine Buckfast the quickest. However, after losing the primitive drinking contest yet again, Gaylord got angry and threw Tormac out of his 19th floor kitchen window to his death. Gaylord and an Alsatian called Ray Pickles still live at No.29 Swine Street, Drumchapel.

Crime News Special

The Trial of Mavis and Mabel Splemm

By our aggressive women reporter *Basil Gopium*

The sensational year-long trial of Mavis and Mabel Splemm at Gubbenstery High Court finally concluded today with a unanimous not guilty verdict. The notorious twin sisters had been charged with 25 counts of murder, 20 counts of arson, and a multitude of other offences including torture, battery, GBH, loan sharking, running protection rackets and one count of deep frying a nosey neighbour. The twins said nothing to a barrage of waiting reporters as they made their way down the steps of the majestic court building, pausing only once for Mavis to punch a reporter in the face and stick a fork into the top of his head.

The twins began life at the age of zero in Goilor Road, South West Gubbenstery on the 20ᵗʰ of April 1960. They were brought up by their doting mother Mrs Splemm and their subnormal but aggressive father Mr Splemm. At the age of five, the twins started at Narlypop Primary School and immediately started as they meant to go on. In the first week alone they had locked another child inside a metal bin with a ferret, set fire to the teacher's skirt and eaten the classroom gerbil. For their misdemeanours they were beaten to a pulp by the headmaster and banned for a month. On noticing the beating administered to his daughters, Mr Splemm went to the school and knocked the headmaster out with a camping mallet before dragging him onto the roof and throwing him off. The headmaster became impaled on the school fence and immediately decided to take early retirement. After that, the twins went through primary school doing anything they wanted. This included demanding money from other kids or they would shave their heads and paint their scalp with tar. They also took money from the teachers after threatening to burn their house down. The twins soon noticed that they only needed to carry a threat to get what they wanted. They rarely had to act on their threats, although they did enjoy doing so from time to time.

Mavis and Mabel then attended Scoblion Secondary School and continued in the same vein. By now the girls had stretched and filled out quite a bit. They were both surprisingly muscular and had hair-trigger tempers. One wrong look and fists and available weapons would be brought into action. They were suspended numerous times but it didn't bother them. They already knew everything they needed to make a living. They left school at sixteen but neither of them could get a job due to their excessive aggression at the interview stage. Usually, when innocently asked, *"Why do you want to work here?"* they would attack whoever was in the room and then start a fire. They eventually joined the Gubbenstery Women's Royal Defence League and initially did well. They came top in all the athletic events, especially boxing, but were poor at baking, knitting and dressmaking. They eventually fell out with their commanding officer because he didn't issue them with live ammunition. One evening, they grabbed him and knocked him out with a monkey wrench. When he came to he was in the regimental kitchen being boiled in a giant pot of water with the twins clubbing him over the head with a cricket bat. He was eventually rescued by the police and fire brigade but he never walked again. Or spoke or ate solid food.

The twins were sent to Gomperston women's prison for five years but served ten years due to repeated violent outbursts. It was while inside that they met Rita McGoon, a lifer who filled their heads with ideas. On their release, the twins went back to their mum's house and used their old room as the epicentre of their criminal empire. Mr Splemm was now serving ten years in prison for an attempted lobotomy on a man who owed him money. Mavis and Mabel had now developed their own individual personalities. Mavis was the brains of the outfit and planned all their activities. She also excelled at violence and advanced persuasive techniques. Mabel was definitely not the brains of the outfit. She simply excelled at extreme violence. After a few years operating out of their mother's house, they had built up a small crew of trusted individuals, both men and women. The women were all large lesbians and the men were all aggressive morons, easily manipulated by Mavis. They all had their roles in what the twins called "The Division," with Mavis as the leader and Mabel as her enforcer.

By now, their enterprise involved extortion, prostitution, pubs and night clubs and a side line handling stolen goods. They were making a fortune and this enabled the twins to pay off bent policemen, city officials and magistrates. They had virtually acquired a licence to do what they liked by lining the pockets of the right people. However, there was one person they couldn't bribe, no matter how hard they tried. Chief Inspector Nancy Glugly was a career police officer and had made it her sworn duty to bring the Splemm twins to justice. On several occasions she had come close to a conviction, but the Splemms simply paid off or burnt the house down of any witnesses willing to give evidence against them. The twins had things their own way until a rival group of lesbian hoodlums moved into the area. They were led by an extremely violent and unpredictable psychopath called Belinda Rempoid, who had previously been convicted of inflating a former associate with compressed air and then bursting them open with a pin. The rival gang had been slowly muscling in on the twin's endeavours and this caused Mabel to become enraged.

Mavis suggested they bide their time before taking action against their rivals but Mabel was only interested in taking immediate decisive action. She found out that Belinda was hosting a Tupperware party for other lesbian career criminals in a local pub called *The Abscess Tavern* and drew up her plans. On the evening of the 19th of June 1986, Mabel Splemm made her way to the tavern and waited outside in the shadows. She had decided not to ambush Belinda in the dark, but instead to stride into the pub and make a clear statement in front of multiple witnesses. At about 9pm, with the party in full swing, Mabel struck. She brazenly walked into the pub and confronted Belinda, who said, *"Oh look, it's one of the mutant twins"*. At that point, Mabel produced a large axe and swung it at Belinda, chopping off both her legs at the knee. She fell to the floor in agony, but managed to punch Mabel in the face as she fell. This angered the less academic Splemm twin and she proceeded to swing her axe until she had chopped Belinda into tiny pieces. She then looked all the witnesses squarely in the eye and walked out without saying a word. Outside the pub, Mavis had turned up with a petrol bomb, which she hurled through the pub window. The tavern burned to the ground as the twins made their way home for a nice cup of tea. They were eventually rounded up by Nancy Glugly and her team a year later and put on trial. However, by then, all the witnesses had developed either amnesia, bullet wounds or lost the ability to climb high buildings without falling off. With no witnesses and no evidence, the jury found them not guilty although they did suggest that the twins should be fully compensated for being on remand for over a year. They were driven back to Goilor Road by one of their Division and celebrated their freedom by hosting a tea party and arranging for the local police station to be burnt to the ground. Chief Inspector Glugly was transferred to a rural station on the outskirts of Glord City.

Whoopit & Darbox Medical Supplies

Where quality is not an issue!

Whoopit and Darbox are proud to announce the addition of several new products to their vast catalogue of medical supplies and pharmaceuticals. Reginald Whoopit and Ronald Darbox started their medical supply company in 1956 and it has since grown into one of the world's medical supply companies. Over the years, they have provided medication and therapeutic devices for all manner of ailments from lockjaw to inflammation of the larynx. Their treatment of rabies by battering it out of the victim with a baseball bat is now legendary in medical circles. A few of the new products in their portfolio are listed below:

Reconstructive Surgery for the Lap (£500) *+ free hamster delousing brush!*
This cutting edge treatment provides structural support, as well as follow up medication, for people who have suffered a collapsed lap. The lap is encased in rock salt for three months and then gradually manoeuvred back into position, before being exposed to a ray beam to finalise healing. Toasted potassium seeds are then rubbed into the lap to protect it from future collapse. This should leave your lap in fantastic condition and capable of supporting dinner trays and pets up to a certain size.

Nape of the Neck Powder (£600) *+ free parrot beak repair kit!*
This newly developed remedy is a highly purified form of powder that is easily rubbed into the nape of the neck, in order to reduce swelling if bitten by a snake or walrus. The nape of the neck is vulnerable to biting creatures due to its proximity to biting creatures. Our special powder works somehow. See tin for details and free two-for-one eye socket offer.

Glapid Ointment (£700) *+ free framed photograph of a horse's tongue!*
The Glapid is the area of skin at the bottom of the torso between the genitalia at the front and the anus to the rear. This small area is highly prone to many problems including rupture, and ripping due to running too fast or falling onto church railings. Our Glapid ointment, made to a secret recipe including Gnat's throat

fluid, will help reduce Glapid healing time to about two years in the first instance. Always wear gloves and protective goggles when applying Glapid ointment to avoid burning the fingers and bursting the eyes.

Clavicle tablets (£800) + *free worm and millipede quiz book!*
The clavicle is the long length of skin that connects the forehead to the stomach lining. It is made up of two parts, the Glort and the Pinnery, and provides structural support to the kidneys. The Glort and Pinnery are susceptible to rotting and festering due to a lack of mung beans and dog oil in the diet. Our tablets cure this problem by a process known as treatment.

These are only a few of our extensive range of healthcare products for the ill-informed person of today. We know your time is valuable and that is why our products are expensive. For a copy of our full colour catalogue and free sample of high-powered explosives, send your name and bust size to:

Whoopit and Darbox, 1-190 Mediocre Cottages, Sprento Lane, Middlesbuwwa.

The Spanzino Medical Centre

A report on the unusual treatments available at Gubbenstery's newest clinic

By our highly excitable reporter *Ned Stromboli*

The Spanzino Medical Centre is the brainchild of secretive clinician Dr Alberto Spanzino. Very little is known about Dr Spanzino. There is no record of him having studied medicine at any of the usual universities and he never gives interviews. His medical centre first opened its doors one year ago and, despite being very expensive, has been a runaway success. However, more and more stories have emerged from dissatisfied patients who have been overcharged for what they call *"Unusual treatments"*. I managed to track down some of these ex-patients who were willing to make their experiences public and this is what they told me.

Mr Skankor Laboothian, aged 59, hamster trainer, Gubbenstery

I booked myself in to get my conjunctivitis sorted. The receptionist took my details and told me to take a seat in the waiting room. After waiting nearly nine hours, I was called in by Dr Spanzino. He was a tall man with a huge afro haircut. He told me to lie down with my eyes wide open and said the treatment may sting a bit. The second I lay down he turned around and poured boiling hot jam into my eyes. I screamed with pain and instinctively threw a punch, catching Spanzino on the lower scrotum. My eyes and face were burning and as the molten liquid trickled into my mouth I detected it was raspberry flavour. He tried to restrain me but I dived through his legs and crashed out of a second floor window. Luckily, I landed on a poodle, which broke my fall and broke the poodle's legs. The dog owner called an ambulance and a vet. I was treated for third degree burns to the face and the poodle was in traction for two years. I told the police what happened but they just ignored me.

Miss Lucinda Hormobe, aged 59, retired clown, Lower Glord

Bunions had bothered me for years and I decided to get them fixed. In the waiting room there were large video screens showing gruesome medical procedures. I saw a woman giving birth to sextuplets, a man having his lungs removed and an elderly man having an ingrowing forehead removed. It was very unsettling. I was in there for eight hours before being taken to the theatre. When I awoke I was in agony. Both my legs had been amputated. Spanzino was standing over my bed and when I asked him what happened, he told me that it was all perfectly normal. *"Bunions are much easier to remove with the legs amputated,"* he said. When I told him I couldn't give a fuck about the bunions if I have no legs, he shouted at me, *"Shut the fuck up you ungrateful bitch".* He then sedated me and I woke up on some waste ground. I told the police what had happened but they didn't believe me.

Mr Ballard McAlinden, aged 59, dog food taste tester, East Buntyside

I had been in a minor car crash and had bitten through my tongue, severing the tip. I had preserved the severed tip in a bag of frozen onions and Dr Spanzino was to reattach it. When I came round, following the operation, I knew something wasn't quite right. My tongue felt too big and heavy. I staggered to the toilet and looked in the mirror. What I saw shocked me so much I nearly laid an egg. My tongue was about two feet long and was hanging out of my mouth, making me drool like a rabid dog. I could now lick the back of my head, which was concerning. When I confronted Spanzino, using a series of grunts and yowls, he said my own bit of tongue had perished when they were washing it in the dishwasher and they had to quickly use an alternative. He said a giraffe had died at the zoo and they decided to attach the giraffe tongue to my tongue and thought that I would like a bigger tongue. I ran out of the building straight to the police station but they said they couldn't do anything because no crime had been committed.

Miss Primrose Lungoil, aged 59, 100m sprinter, Skonkage

I had suffered for years with heartburn and, following a consultation with Dr Spanzino, had decided to have my stomach gently cleaned with saline. I was assured by Dr Spanzino that this was a simple procedure, so I signed up for it at a cost of £29,000. When I awoke, I was lying on the floor of the gents' toilet in a pool of blood and urine. I was in agony. My belly was totally distended and felt like it weighed ten tons. I eventually got to my feet and staggered out of the toilet to seek help. I saw Spanzino playing on a pinball machine so I shouted to him for help. He immediately told me to *"Shut the fuck up"* 'cos he nearly had the high score. He failed to get the high score and approached me while chuntering to himself and swearing. When I told him I thought something was wrong, he said nothing was wrong. He had completely removed my stomach to give it a wash but he accidentally dropped it on the floor. Before he could bend down to pick it up, the departmental dog, a pit-bull called Desmond Flannery, grabbed it and ate it. He knew he would need to quickly find a substitute stomach so that I could eat my dinner, so they used an empty twenty gallon beer keg that was lying outside the social club. He went on to assure me that I definitely wouldn't suffer heartburn again. He also said he'd take a tenner off the price as a gesture of goodwill. When I asked how I ended up on the floor of the gents' toilet, he said they needed the bed so they threw me in there on a temporary basis. I burst into tears and fled the clinic. When I arrived at the police station to make an official complaint the two policemen on duty burst out laughing. They said they'd never heard anything so ridiculous and told me to piss off home.

Mr Teddy Gimpitus, aged 20, High Court Judge, Western Gubbenstery

My trip to the Spanzino Medical Centre should have been a routine procedure. I was getting a traffic cone removed from my anus that I had accidentally fallen backwards onto. Dr Spanzino told me that quite a few men fell backwards onto traffic cones these days and removal took about five minutes and was completely painless. I was all ready for the operation, lying on my side in my bed, when Dr Spanzino entered the room carrying a medium-sized sledgehammer and asked me if I could help him hang a picture. I didn't feel that great but I thought I'd lend a hand. As I stood up, he swung the hammer and crashed a savage blow onto the top of my head and knocked me clean out. The next thing I remember is waking up lying on the floor in a dimly lit corridor. I was in utter agony. My head was split open and had been crudely stitched together with some sort of heavy duty wire. I scrambled to my feet to sit on a nearby chair and only then realised the traffic cone was still stuck up me. Spanzino then appeared and told me they had run out of anaesthetic and he had to use the sledgehammer method of anaesthesiology. He couldn't remove the traffic cone because it was in too deep but I'd learn to live with it. I left the centre in tears and in agony and told my story to the police. They thought it was a practical joke and told me to sod off and not waste their time.

The Spanzino Medical Centre is still in business but is under investigation by Gubbenstery Health Board. As a footnote, it appears that Dr Spanzino's brother, Professor Zebedee Spanzino, is being lined up to become head of the Canine Hysterectomy Department at Gubbenstery University.

Outdoor and Indoor Bargains

Heavy drinker requires chatty, fun companions for morning, afternoon and evening drinking sessions. Nibbles (dog food), TV (black and white, no sound) and chairs (boxes) available at no charge. Wife (large) available at small extra charge. Come on over to Georgie Stewpot's house and let the fun begin. 130,000 South Fecundity Street, Glord.

In-Car Foot Spa
In the summer months you need to cool your feet while driving. Foot spas plug into the cigarette lighter and sit adjacent to the accelerator. Simply take your foot off the gas and submerge it in a relaxing foam bath. No need to stop. Two speeds, off and on. Insert one or both feet at the same time to bathe your tootsies. £91.06 each.

Garden Hoses
Treat yourself to a new hose. We only charge by the inch. Cut to the length we want. £3 per cubic acre of hose. Offer does not apply to pantyhose.

Train to be a stuntman with ex-Hollywood stuntman Archie Nackris. Learn how to bite a hammer, sleep under water, punch a leopard, eat a dead cat, jump off the back of a moving pig, trip over a wasp and so much more. Write to Archie at Pummel House, 321 Wallop Quadrant, Gubbenstery.

Babysitter required for deaf cat. Lucky is a 20 year-old tabby and is still full of life. Experience of cat food, fur balls and half-eaten mice would be an advantage. Phone Tina Snud on East Buntyside 301.

Gardener required for small window box. This is a full-time position requiring a gardener for a small window box. Part-time non-gardeners need not apply. Write to Vippo or Nobbo McPoon on Gubbenstery 1000.

Diverse set of misshapen children available to buy or rent. Email Miss Euphemia Dismal on Glord 007.

Opening in December, our new Naked Photography Department will provide all your naked photographic needs including boy-girl, girl-girl, girl-horse and nun-priest.

The Hunt for Ron Gasim and Keith Bem

By our tallest woman reporter *Big Kay Gerbil*

Gubbenstery Police have issued an urgent appeal for information leading to the arrest of two highly dangerous conmen. Ron Gasim and Keith Bem have been on a massive crime spree, preying on highly gullible people up and down the UK. They have relieved thick and greedy people of their money by making them offers that are too good to refuse. The man leading the investigation into the activities of Gasim and Bem, Detective Superintendent Sergeant Jacko Skunby of Gubbenstery Police says these despicable men have to be apprehended quickly. Ron Gasim, although only five feet tall, is a deceptively tall man. The most recent description of him is that he was dressed as an emu and wearing a blindfold. Keith Bem is a deceptively short man, despite being six feet tall, and was last seen disguised as a naked man, also wearing a blindfold.

Gasim and Bem commenced their latest crime spree in Northern Stornoway, a beautiful island on the outskirts of Scotland. They set up a stall in the centre of town selling planets for £100 each and sold out almost immediately. One of the gullible idiots who purchased a planet was local layabout Fritz Gershwin, who bought Neptune. It was only when he found out that Neptune was 2.7 billion miles away that he had second thoughts. His 1965 Ford Anglia had just failed its MOT so he realised that a trip to Neptune was out of the question. Six months later he immediately voiced his concern to local policeman PC Moshe Milligram, who wrote to DSS Skunby. By that time, Gasim and Bem had scarpered.

The two crooks set up their next devious crime in the beautiful village of Llyyllyyll in Wales, where again they targeted easily fleeceable, dim-witted shoppers in the High Street. This time, Gasim and Bem were selling talking pelicans. This latest scam was even more successful than their planet sale. A temporary booth with a giant picture of a toy pelican on the top was set up by Gasim and Bem outside Dafydd Bloodflow and Sons Butchers shop. The idea was that for only £500 you could have your very own talking pelican, when they arrive on the boat from Tanzania in a month or two. They claimed demand was high and you would need to act fast if you wanted one. People were soon queuing round the block and handing over their money in their droves to secure one of these "very rare" yakking birds. This latest outrage only came to light when it was reported by local racoon salesman, Alfredo Zanetti, 59, to Q Division of the Llyyllyyll Constabulary. He said he had rushed to meet the postman every morning in the hope that he would receive his preposterous pet. However, after five years of waiting, he began to lose hope of ever acquiring the stupid thing, so he gave it another five years before reporting what he thought might be a crime. By that time, Gasim and Bem had scarpered.

Reports from Interpol and items in Sunday newspaper colour supplements suggested that Gasim and Bem had switched from fraud to armed robbery. Their modus operandi was simple. They would enter the premises to be robbed and hold up the staff using a bow and arrow. According to sources close to Scotland Yard, Gasim and Bem carried out over 4,000 armed robberies in only three weeks, mainly in the Cotswolds and surrounding area. They were never clearly identified due to their brilliant disguises but one 92 year-old lady, Mrs Agatha Froth of Narley-on-the-Pomp, said she saw a giant squirrel and what looked like an octopus leaving her local bank when the alarm was sounding, although she did admit to being *"completely steamboats"* drunk at the time. The only connection between the robberies and Gasim and Bem was that the most recent establishment to be robbed was Archibald Nitrate's pet shop in the rural hamlet of Chipping-on-the-Chopping where around 3,000 talking pelicans were stolen.

After lying low for about a year, Gasim and Bem were soon up to their old tricks in Central London. Once again they set up one of their fake booths in Oxford Street, where they set about selling a special rare breed of cattle. According to their well-polished monologue, these special multi-tasking cows would deliver over 100 litres of milk from their udders and produce around 50 solid bricks of cheese from their anus every day. A photograph of a cow adorned the front of their booth and once again queues were long. It appeared that people were keener than ever to be parted from their money. Apparently Gasim and Bem sold over 100 cows at £1,000 each before disappearing. Detective Colonel Ziggy Thompson of Scotland Yard said they only became aware of the bovine crime following a complaint from a local resident. Mum-of-ten Lee-Anne Vermin, 29, said she had placed an order for one of the cows using the last of her child benefit money. She said the vast quantities of milk and cheese supplied by the beast would be handy for her multiple offspring. She had already set up a byre in her oldest son's bedroom whilst he was serving five years in prison. Darren Wayne Lee Vermin, 20, had recently been convicted of pulling off a man's scrotum who allegedly owed him money. By that time, Gasim and Bem had scarpered. When I asked Miss Vermin how she felt about being conned out of £1,000 she said, *"It's like, what the fuck, a mean, fuck that, like, fuck it, a don't give a fuck,"* as she headed off with her brood to the local council to demand more child benefit money.

The last known sighting of Gasim and Bem was in Benidorm, where they were seen drinking in Big Malky McTavish's Pub. Spanish police were alerted but were out of luck when they raided Malky's. Gasim and Bem had disappeared and Big

Malky himself had no idea when they might be back by the way. However, the police did seize considerable quantities of milk, cheese and a noisy seabird. Enquiries are ongoing and police are hopeful of an arrest soon for no apparent reason. DSS Skunby suggests if you see either Gasim or Bem do not take any unnecessary risks. He cannot stress this strongly enough – these are highly dangerous men. Try to approach both of them from behind by leaping on them from a height. Immediately start punching and kicking them until you are satisfied you have administered a substantial beating and rendered them unconscious, obviously using the minimum of force. When they are subdued, put them under a citizen's arrest and hand them in to your local police station.

Spizzly and Poheedron Fundament Care

Preserving the Buttocks since 1873

Products for the Arse

Bumshine (£50 per can or two for £120)

Bumshine is our very latest product for producing a brilliant high gloss finish to your bum. No matter how dull your arse may be, Bumshine will produce a fantastic finish you can be proud of when you're naked. You'll want to display your backside at every opportunity once you acquire the Bumshine shine.

Arsoscaff (£100 per starter Kit; additional poles £1 each)

Arsoscaff is an easy-to-use arse scaffolding kit which helps prop up the saggiest of derrieres. The kit consists of lightweight aluminium scaffolding poles joined together using heavy duty couplers with associated wooden access boards. Arsoscaff is designed to fit any shape of shitcan and fits snugly under the trousers or skirt.

Arse Corks (Available in packs of 190 for £29 or 191 for £129)

Made from 100% Portuguese cork, these robust and durable anal bungs are ideal for the modern flatulent person of today. Insert one in the morning and you will be safe all day from letting rip at bus stops, business meetings or public speaking engagements. Take a ride in a lift or go to bed with a stranger safe in the knowledge that all your gaseous waste will be redirected elsewhere.

Arse Masks (Strapped Arse Mask £62 or Glued Arse Mask £1.62)

Arse masks are essential for the modern person of today who requires a fully presentable dungbox. Arse masks are made from lightweight and durable clay and can be configured to fit any rear end. They are designed to strengthen a weak arse and prevent collapse or plummeting of the bowels. They can be strapped on or glued on using industrial solvent to give complete peace of mind even when performing difficult manoeuvres like lying on your arse, falling on your arse or fighting your next door neighbour.

Musical Arse Plugs (£18 per plug or 3 for £11)

Make use of unwanted or offensive bum vapours by inserting a musical arse plug into your nipsy. Each of these innovative inserts plays a different tune which discretely conceals any rip-roaring anal acoustics. Instead of suffering an embarrassing bum belch, why not enjoy a beautiful snippet of classical music or the friendly bark of an Alsatian dog or even the joy of a crying baby. Musical Arse Plugs take the strain out of unexpected turbulent rear end blasts.

For free full colour catalogue and complimentary 19-litre can of luminous buttock paint, send only £17.09 to Spizzly and Poheedron Curious and Astonishing Products Ltd, No.1 Large Bum Plaza, Polio Industrial Estate, Wartsinall Street, Northwest Gubbenstery.

Exhilarating New Board Games
By
Golden Uterus Board Games
In association with
Bulbourethral Pastimes

By our quite gullible reporter *Bartholomew Quaizoid*

The brand new collection of cutting-edge and innovative board games from the Golden Uterus Company will be going on sale in selected stores tomorrow. Following their recent merger with Bulbourethral Pastimes, Golden Uterus has gone from strength to strength. Chairman Terry Paloorian, speaking at the Gubbenstery Business Convention last week commented, *"The merger was a fucking spiffing idea"*. He then added, *"It's fucking magic. Our games are selling like fucking hot cakes."* Board game enthusiasts have been queuing for days in the hope of getting their hands on one of the much sought after new games. Our reporter Bartholomew Quaizoid has had a sneak preview of some of the best new games and sends this report right now.

Moth or Mouse
A game for 1-100 players aged 26-29, this is a thrill-a-minute cracker. Each person is given clues and the answer will be either moth or mouse. Answering correctly gets you £59 from each of the other players. Giving an incorrect answer, for example saying moth when the answer is mouse, incurs a forfeit. Forfeits range from being hit in the teeth with a large spoon, to being locked inside the nearest radiator for one hour. Very exciting indeed.

Pain in the Arse
Players sit naked around the "Board of Pain" and throw a dice to start. Whoever throws a number between 1 and 6 goes first. Each person has a "Razor Blade of Pain" in their mouth and when it's their turn they spit it onto the board. Wherever it lands designates what type of pain in the arse they get. For example, landing on the square with a picture of a shoe on it means all the other players kick your arse once. Landing on a picture of a rabbit means you have two large slices cut off your arse and fed to the nearest rabbit. Alternatively, you might land on the square

containing a picture of a bile duct. This is one to avoid because landing on this means you have your bile duct pulled out through your rectum by the person to your left. There are 150 different squares to land on, so there is a wide variety of arse pain in store for each player. The winner is the person with the most complete arse after the 6-week game is finished. This one really is fun all the way.

Neighbours

This is a game for 9 or 11 players. There are 35 dice in a cup and each person takes a turn to throw them. The first person to get 35 sixes with one throw is the "Boss" and they stay in the house while the rest go to different neighbours' houses. The object of the game is to stay in the neighbour's house as long as possible. One point is scored for every day you can stay in the neighbour's house. Anyone returning to the house within a month is tarred and feathered. The winner is the first person to stay in a neighbour's house for a year. A real thriller.

Count the Butter

This game is for adults only and can be very risqué if it gets out of hand. The day before the game is played, one person goes around the house and smears butter at 20 different locations. The game is commenced when the person with the longest toes throws a pack of unsalted butter out of an open window. Each player then takes it in turn to search the house for the butter smears. To aid counting, each time they find a butter smear each player hammers a 3-inch nail into the back of their hand to act as a tally counter. Surprisingly, the winner is not the person with the most nails in the back of their hand. The winner is the player with the most vowels in their name. In the event of a tie, the winner is the person who can fall flat on their face the quickest. A totally hilarious way to spend an afternoon.

Yuckybuckybimbam

This is a real laugh-a-minute board game reminiscent of some of the classic board games of yesteryear. A simple-looking board has 10 white squares and 10 black squares. On each white square there is a pint of whisky and on each black square there is pint of "Ferocious Lemonade", which is a mixture of pulped earthworms, 10 whole chillies, dog blood and buttermilk, all exquisitely blended into freshly made country-style lemonade. The game commences when the player with the lowest forehead turns over the first of the "Cards of Spume". On the card there will be a picture of an animal and the player that resembles it most has to drink 5 white squares and 5 black squares. When the drinks are consumed, the drinker is then savagely punched in the stomach by all the other players. Whoever is still conscious after two months is the winner and they get to iron the back of the head of all the other players. A real highbrow classic.

Doggy or Moggy

Real concentration is needed for this mind-bending new addition to Golden Uterus's game collection for the under-fives. Between 15 and 17 players sit around a table and play a standard game of Texas Hold'em Poker. The winner then moves onto phase 2 where they choose a cat and a dog from the animal bin and tie their tails together. All the other players then start ringing loud bells and banging cymbals together for 2 hours. The cat and dog will react poorly to the din and try to escape. Players can then bet up to a third of their winnings on which animal will lose the most amount of fur, doggy or moggy. The players with the three best guesses win one quarter of a third of a steak pie and 20 complimentary cigarettes of their choice. All the losing players have to eat three slices of Cat and Dog Cake and have their tongue pierced. The game ends when either 28 more rounds are played or the klaxon is sounded by the robotic gerbil. Kids will love it.

Cheating Bastard

This is a real fun game for all the family. A standard deck of cards is mixed with a non-standard deck of cards and each player is given one card face up. If you have a red card, the person to your right pulls your hair for an hour. If you have a black card, the person to your left kicks your knee for an hour. If you have an ace, the person opposite you gets 3 goes at hitting you on the chin with a large ball bearing fired from a high-powered catapult. After 10 rounds of mayhem and screaming, everyone puts a blindfold on and the game continues. At exactly 14 hours into the game, the person who secretly brought the hand gun starts firing it indiscriminately at the other players. The winner is the first of the players being shot at to shout "*Cheating Bastard*" 148 times. Innocent but amusing family fun.

Gubbenstery Theme Pubs Guide No. 2

Let's go out and get befuddled!

The Brain Stem Bar

Landlord Mr Arthur Cadmium would like to extend a warm invitation to all his customers to take part in this week's theme night. Everyone who arrives on horseback or riding a cat will get a special voucher which will enable them to buy any number of alcoholic drinks. A special prize of a 100-yard length of wooden fencing will be awarded to anyone arriving on the back of a baboon. 76 Fudd Avenue, Gubbenstery.

The Crowded Pussy Fun Pub

Come along to the Pussy this Saturday night dressed as either a horse or a pencil and get a free sheep's head roasted in lard. All drinks guaranteed full price. 74 Thong Avenue, Gubbenstery.

The Bloodboy and Baby

Gubbenstery's eighteenth oldest pub is the place to be on a Monday night. This week, anyone dressed as a murderer will win a hunting knife, ten pints of super lager and a bottle of single malt whisky (which must be consumed on the premises). 80 Barney Glucose Plaza, Gubbenstery.

Rupert Wartboy's Gastrointestinal Pub

Enjoy a memorable dining experience or simply pop in for a cocktail on one of our themed evenings. This Friday we are running a special disembowelment evening where one lucky customer will be disembowelled by our Michelin-starred chef Marcel Gummo and the stomach contents used to prepare a lavish banquet for our Drink-a-Yard-of-Urine competition winner. Dogs, cats and mice welcome. 78 Faghag Terrace, Gubbenstery.

The Boozy Dogpig Bar

Thursday night is party night. After 10pm all drinks are free. Children and pets welcome. Everyone who brings a fully grown chimpanzee will be entered into our prize draw to win a brand new turnip trimming knife. 88 South Lavatory Road, Gubbenstery.

The Human Bastard Inn

Enjoy an evening of competitive naked wrestling against our resident champion Chief Inspector Finbarr Timotay.